ABOVE ALL

A PHYSICIAN

RENÉ THÉOPHILE LAENNEC

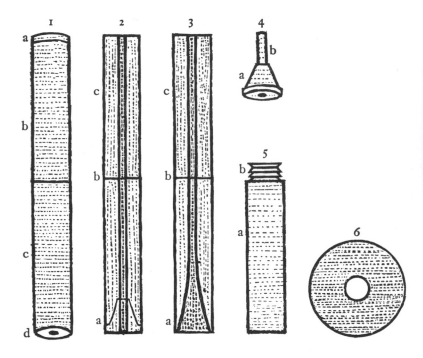

**PORTIONS OF ORIGINAL STETHOSCOPE,
INVENTED BY RENÉ THÉOPHILE LAENNEC**

1. A MOUNTED STETHOSCOPE: a. *extremity to be placed on subject with stem in place;* b. *lower half;* c. *upper half;* d. *hearing extremity.*

2. A MOUNTED STETHOSCOPE, *inside view;* c. *upper half;* b. *point of union of both parts;* a. *stem in place.*

3. SAME WITHOUT STEM

4. STEM: a. *body of the stem of the same wood as the stethoscope;* b. *short copper stem fastened in the stethoscope.*

5. UPPER HALF OF THE STETHOSCOPE: a. *the body;* b. *screw permitting the union of the two halves.*

6. EXACT DIAMETER OF THE STETHOSCOPE

ABOVE ALL
A PHYSICIAN

RENÉ THÉOPHILE LAENNEC

1781–1826

BY *Jeanne Carbonnier*

CHARLES SCRIBNER'S SONS

New York

TO

Marcelle,

René

and

Denise Laridan,

U. S. 1454016

affectionately

J.C.

*Grateful acknowledgment is made for help
in documentation to the following:*

M. F. DU FRETAY
owner of Kerlouarnec
DR. EDOUARD MAHÉO
M. JEAN MOREL
MME. ANNE MOULINNEUF

CONTENTS

ABOVE ALL
A PHYSICIAN
RENÉ THÉOPHILE LAENNEC

✜ CHAPTER 1

A gray February morning of the year 1788. It was drizzling as it often does in Brittany. On a deserted road a lone gig was plodding along in the mist that shrouded sky and forest alike. Moisture dripping onto his shoulders from his wide-brimmed hat, the driver let the horse take a slow pace, as if time did not matter to the three passengers huddled under the hood.

Suddenly the horse perked up. The first houses of Quimper had emerged from the fog, and at the bend of the road the carriage entered a street leading to the bank of the Odet River.

The jarring clatter of the wheels on the cobblestones woke Father Michel Laennec, who had fallen asleep, his breviary in his hands. One of his two companions, a boy of seven with clear eyes and reddish hair, had been looking out the window since they left the rectory at Elliant. Bent forward to see better, turning his head from one side to the other, he paid no attention to the rain that trickled from the hood.

The other boy, a year younger, had been keeping the priest company in a deep slumber.

Father Laennec closed his prayer book, smothered a yawn, and asked in a sleepy voice, "Still raining, Théophile?"

The boy who was watching the scenery answered without turning his head, "Yes, Uncle."

"Glad to get home, Théophile?"

There was an imperceptible silence before Théophile said, "Yes, Uncle, but I'll miss my friends . . . and I'll miss you also, Uncle."

Another silence, then Théophile spoke again: "Do you think Marie-Anne will know me? She was so little when we left a year ago."

"She won't be home, Théophile. I told you she is still in Vitré with your aunt, and Vitré is far from Quimper."

"Perhaps Papa will take her back now that we are going to be home, Michaud and I. It would be so nice to be together again as . . . as . . . when Maman was there."

The uncle did not answer. He raised himself to put his breviary in his pocket and shook the other boy gently. "Wake up, Michaud."

Michaud grunted but did not open his eyes.

Théophile continued, still looking outside, "Me, Michaud, no Marie-Anne. It won't be as before. . . ." And pointing at a house: "Uncle, we are home."

The horse had stopped before a mansion, and quickly Théophile jumped out and ran to the door. He stretched on his toes and tried to reach the heavy brass knocker. He succeeded in lifting it and it fell back with a resounding thud. He laughed and turned to his uncle, who was helping the sleepy Michaud out of the gig. "I could not bang it last year. Now I can. I'm taller." He listened for steps inside and giggled. "Papa will be surprised. He didn't expect us so soon."

"He certainly will be surprised," answered the priest.

A woman's face, topped with the pointed lace cap of the region, appeared at the peephole and, in a burst of joyful exclamations, she flung open the door.

Théophile threw himself into her arms. "Maria!"

She looked at him with admiration. "Théophile, how you have grown."

"Yes, and I can lift the knocker now."

"And Michaud! He is a little man." She freed herself from the children's embrace. "Good morning, *monsieur le curé*. Please excuse me. I should have asked you to come in first but I'm so happy to see the boys again."

The three travelers entered, glad to escape the penetrating drizzle, and Maria kept on: "Won't the master be surprised. He is upstairs. He had given strict orders not to be disturbed but this is different. I'll call him."

The priest stopped her. "Take the children with you. I want to speak to my brother first."

Maria lifted Michaud in her arms and took Théophile's hand. "Come with me to the kitchen. I'll give each of you a big glass of milk and I'll make some buckwheat crêpes for your luncheon."

Left alone, the priest went to the stairway. Half muffled by the thick curtains, the sound of a voice reached his ears as he climbed the creaky steps. " 'Your beauty, my Jeannette, fills my heart,' " the voice declaimed. There was a pause, then again: " 'Your beauty, Jeannette mine . . .' Ah, 'Jeannette mine' is better. . . . 'Your beauty . . .' "

The priest knocked at the door. No answer. He knocked again.

"By Jove," said the voice impatiently, "can't I have peace? . . . And your beauty . . . Now the inspiration is gone. What is it?"

"Open, Théo. It is I, Michel."

The door opened and the two brothers faced each other.

"Michel! I did not expect you today. Come in. Excuse me. I had given orders not to be disturbed. I wanted to finish this bit of poetry for a party tonight."

The priest looked at the papers on the desk. "I see you still are a poet. I heard you from the staircase and for a moment I even thought you were in Jeannette's company."

Théo Laennec grinned and drew two armchairs near the fire. "First, Michel, my heartiest congratulations. It is an honor to be the brother of the canon and rector of the Collège at Tréguier. What a leap from the vicarate at Elliant." And with a friendly slap on Michel's knee, "I'm proud of you."

Refusing to acknowledge the compliment with so much as a smile, Michel addressed the exuberant Théo coldly: "Your children are here."

"Ah." And with the same tone he had used to celebrate Jeannette's beauty, Théo exclaimed, "My little sons, how I missed them."

"You won't miss them any more. As I have advised you in my last message, I can't take them to Tréguier with me. You'll have to be a father again and act the part."

Théo spoke in a dramatic voice. "How can I, a lonely widower, charged with the responsibilities of tax collector, give my little darlings the love and attention they need?"

"You mean that you are not fit to be a father? This, my dear Théo, is everybody's opinion. In the months that followed their mother's death you proved it. That is why I took your sons and your sister-in-law took Marie-Anne. Now you'll have to mend your ways, pay your debts, forsake dinners, parties, and the rest because the children will stay with you."

Théo tried a last argument. "I'm thinking of going to Paris in the near future." No answer. He insisted, "Paris . . . Versailles, delightful company at the court of our good King Louis XVI."

Michel cut in sharply, "Seems to me you are quite ready to drop the responsibilities of your charge."

Théo dismissed the remark with a flick of his well-groomed hands on his lace cuffs and asked, "Do you expect me to take the children to Paris?"

"I expect you to take care of them. As for your plans to leave Quimper, they won't mature. I've learned to know you. Your children deserve the warmth of a real home. Théophile, your namesake, is a sensitive child, gay, affectionate, intelligent. Michaud—"

"Your namesake," echoed Théo.

"—Michaud, although younger, shows the same traits. They both need the companionship of their father." And Michel Laennec got up. "You'd better go downstairs and get acquainted with them. I'm staying with you today; tomorrow I continue my trip to Tréguier. May I retire for a while?"

Théo closed the door behind his brother. He sat at his desk, tried to read the unfinished poem, but his mind wandered away from *Jeannette Mine*. He crushed the paper nervously. "My brother has clipped the wings of my inspiration," he mumbled. He reached for a new quill, sharpened it with a few quick strokes, and began writing.

Guillaume, my dear brother, I need your help. Michel is here on his way to Tréguier and he refuses to take the children with him. In other words, he abandons them.

You know what a considerate father I am, thinking only of their welfare. For the sake of their education I feel that I must part with them once more. Confronted with the responsibilities of my position, I could not give them the attention they need. They must have the warmth of a real home, in Michel's very words.

You are a well-established physician, admired and respected by the population of Nantes. You have a wife who could replace the dear one who left me two years ago; you have a young son who will be a desirable companion for them. Guillaume, I beg you to consent to raise my orphaned sons.

Théo Laennec stopped, tickled the tip of his nose with the end of the quill, and smiled with satisfaction. "Good kindhearted Guillaume. He won't say no. He always wanted a large family. He'll jump at this opportunity to give his son two brothers."

His satisfied smile broadened as he sprinkled gold powder on the fresh ink. With an amused grin he pressed his signet into the smoking wax to seal his message. And, feeling he had fulfilled his duty as a father, he returned to *Jeannette Mine*.

⟪ CHAPTER 2

The Breton port of Nantes, on the Loire estuary, was bustling under a gay spring sun. At one of the wharfs the *St. Goustan* was being moored, and on her deck two excited boys were running from one side to the other.

"Théophile," said Michaud, trying to follow his brother, "Théophile! What does he look like, Uncle Guillaume?"

"You've asked me one hundred times," replied Théophile. "For the hundreth time, I don't know. Never saw him."

"Théophile, suppose we don't find him."

"He'll find us. He wrote Papa that he'd meet us at the boat."

"How will he know us if he never saw us?"

"Oh, stop it," said Théophile impatiently. "He'll recognize us."

In spite of his apparent poise, Théophile felt uneasy. "What kind of an uncle is he?" he wondered. "Easygoing

like Uncle Michel? Exuberant and indifferent like Papa?"
His anxiety was somewhat relieved as he remembered the
letter his father had read to him. Uncle Guillaume had
written: "My house, like my heart, is open to them."

The captain was approaching. "My boys, you are home."

Théophile interrupted him. "Nantes is not our home,
sir."

"No," said Michaud, "our home is at Elliant."

"No," corrected Théophile, "our home is at Quimper."
And suddenly he realized they had no home. Deserted by
Uncle Michel, rejected twice by their father, he felt they
were alone in the world. He put his arm around Michaud's
shoulder as if to protect him, and with tears in his voice
he addressed Captain Leroux. "Thank you, sir, for all your
kindness."

Then he turned his eyes toward the quay. A man was
waving from below.

"Here he is, Michaud!" exclaimed Théophile.

The two scrambled down with the speed of acrobats and
found themselves before a tall man resembling their father.
His affectionate welcome dispelled their fear. "My new
sons," he said, "let's go home. Everybody is eager to meet
you. A trunk? I'll send Joseph, my servant, to pick it up
later."

"No, Uncle, two small bundles."

As they walked to their uncle's buggy Théophile noted

how cordially the passers-by greeted Uncle Guillaume. He
replied to some in Breton, to others in French. He even
spoke a foreign language to a group of sailors and, to Théophile's question, answered that he had lived two years in
England.

A short ride took them to the Place du Bouffay, a large
square, lined with trees.

"Here is your new home," said Uncle Guillaume, rein-
ing the horse, "and there is your aunt Désirée with Cousin
Christophe."

Before they could reach the door a dog jumped on them
joyously.

"Mirza, down!"

"A dog!" Théophile felt like hugging him before anyone else. Quickly he grabbed Michaud's hand to be sure
he would not greet Mirza first and they both kissed their
aunt.

Aunt Désirée was everything Théophile had wanted
her to be—pretty, gay, affectionate, like the mother he
scarcely remembered. He loved her as soon as he heard her
musical voice and saw her vivacious smile.

As for three-year-old Christophe, he gave each of his
new cousins a most resounding kiss to seal their friendship.

"Now, children, let's go up," Aunt Désirée said. "We
have an apartment, not a house. Come and meet my mother.
You probably know she is living with us."

Madame de Gennes was waiting in the living room. She dropped her embroidery and opened her arms. "So, these are my new grandchildren." And a throaty voice screamed, "*Bon . . . Bon . . . Bonjour!*" Jacquot the parrot had joined in the welcome.

Théophile looked around him. "This is my home," he thought. "I did not know it would be like this." And, overcome by his emotion, he burst into tears.

It did not take long for Théophile and Michaud to get accustomed to their new life. Still, Théophile missed the country, and when summer came and Uncle Guillaume opened his cottage at Petit-Port, he was overjoyed. There were swimming and boating parties on the Erdre. Occasionally Uncle Guillaume appeared for a short stay and the days they spent together were to live forever in Théophile's memory. Théophile's curiosity was endless, Uncle Guillaume knew everything, and he never refused to answer any questions. Little by little Théophile learned the rudiments of botany.

At long intervals letters came from Papa Laennec. He was too busy squandering money, dodging creditors, and writing poetry to his many ladies fair to worry about his sons. However, Uncle Guillaume tactfully kept alive in their hearts the respect and love due to a father.

In the fall Théophile started school. Every morning he

trotted diligently to the Institution Tardivel; every afternoon he came home at four o'clock unless poor marks or disobedience had won him extra hours of study.

One bright morning in 1790, Théophile was awakened by a beaming uncle. "Théophile," he said, "you have a new cousin. Your aunt and I would be pleased to have you be Baby Ambroise's godfather."

The wording of the request, the honor bestowed on him, the importance of his new title made Théophile proud and happy. He jumped out of bed yelling, "I accept!" and could not wait to meet his godchild. He was disappointed to find him so small and so unresponsive to his kiss, but he loved him just the same. Feeling very grown up, on the eleventh of June he signed the baptismal register in the Church of the Sainte Croix: René Théophile Laennec.

Although Nantes was quiet, the political situation in Paris was deteriorating rapidly. The Revolution was on the march since La Bastille had been stormed and taken by an unruly mob on July 14, 1789. Gradually stripped of his power, Louis XVI, after an ill-fated attempt to leave the country in June 1791, was arrested with the royal family. The Republic was proclaimed on September 22, 1792, and France was then ruled by an assembly, the Convention Nationale, which was to send the King to the guillotine on January 21, 1793.

In the spring of 1792, when Théophile left the Institution Tardivel to become a pupil of the Oratorian Fathers, the King was in prison. Panic spread, and entire families sought shelter in foreign countries. When churches and convents were ordered closed, nuns and priests emigrated or went into hiding. Through a secret channel Uncle Michel sent word that he was leaving for Southhampton.

Meanwhile Brittany and her sister province, Vendée, rose against the government of the Convention. Peasants armed with scythes, knives, and guns attacked the soldiers of the newly proclaimed Republic. Reprisals followed. In March 1793, after news of the King's execution reached the west, guerrillas formed organized bands. Alarmed at the extension of the revolt, the Paris government decided to crush it ruthlessly.

One day, coming from school, Théophile saw a large crowd in the Place du Bouffay around a newly erected platform.

"Funny-looking house," thought Théophile, and he glanced at his home. Joseph was watching from the balcony, a sure sign that Aunt Désirée was not in. "I have time," concluded Théophile, "I must see what they are building." He pushed his way through. Some men were lifting a large triangular sheet of metal from a wagon.

"Hey, don't cut your fingers," someone yelled. Scattered laughs answered him.

Quickly the men adjusted the metal to the framework and one of them pulled a cord. An awed murmur rose from the crowd as the blade fell with a deep thud.

"Anyone willing to try it?" he jeered, resetting it.

"Oh," Théophile said, "a guillotine."

He pushed his way toward his house and climbed upstairs rapidly. He was right. Aunt Désirée was not home; neither were Michaud and Christophe. Madame de Gennes had closed the door of her room. Théophile went to the parlor. Joseph was still on the balcony.

"Where is my aunt?" he inquired.

"She's gone with the doctor to see about the completion of the new house."

"I know," said Théophile, "Place Royale."

"Place Egalité," corrected Joseph. "Those who say 'Royale' will get shortened over there on that scaffold."

Joseph had never spoken so boldly before. A queer feeling seized Théophile. He did not know what to say and stood there on the balcony, fascinated by the odd-looking machine.

"I think I'll leave you soon," said Joseph. "I'm going to enlist in the Armies of the Republic. Before I go I'll teach Jacquot to scream, 'Death to the aristocrats!' "

As he spoke, a key turned in the lock. Aunt Désirée, Uncle Guillaume, and the children were back. Joseph decamped and Jacquot yelled, *"Bon . . . Bon . . . Bon-jour."*

Quicker than Christophe and Michaud, Aunt Désirée had run to the window and shut it. "Don't open it," ordered Uncle Guillaume.

"It is horrifying," Aunt Désirée said, burying her face in her hands. "The guillotine right under our apartment and the new house won't be ready for at least three months. What a sight for the children. God have mercy on us!"

And for three months the Laennecs had to face the gruesome spectacle of frequent executions. From March to June there were forty-eight beheadings.

Aunt Désirée and her mother always took refuge at the other end of the apartment in spite of the order that the windows be kept open and that everyone witness and applaud "the just punishment of the enemies of the Revolution."

It was almost impossible to drag the children away from the balcony. Encouraged by Joseph, who never missed being there, they would escape from the back room and watch.

Crowds gathered early. They shouted their approval to the executioner as he worked the blade up and down first, and from afar came a mournful song. The tumbril was near. It came into view. Cries of "To death" greeted the condemned, drowning their religious song. One by one

they were tied to the machine and the blade fell. Howls
from the mob covered the prayers of those who waited for
their doom below the scaffold.

Michaud had been quick to learn the *"ça ira, ça ira"*
that he heard at each execution. He and Christophe sang
it to Joseph's amusement and to the family's dismay. Théophile never spoke, neither did he sing. He just looked.
And Jacquot did not learn to say, "Death to the aristocrats."

Strangely enough, life was not disrupted. Théophile
continued to attend the Oratory, now called the Institution
Nationale and staffed with lay teachers. Most of its priests
had emigrated but its former headmaster, Father Fouché
de Rouzerolles, had foresaken his vows and had been named
deputy to the Convention.

Théophile studied geography, mathematics, French, and
the new constitution in the reorganized school. In his spare
time he wrote poetry.

In June, as the number of executions increased, Guillaume
Laennec decided to move to the new house, finished or not.
Life had become unbearable. Now there were more than
twenty executions every day.

At that time a grave danger faced Nantes. Partisans loyal
to the monarchy—the Chouans, as they were called after
one of their leaders, Jean Chouan—were approaching. They
had been victorious north and south of the Loire and the

rumor had spread that they were ready to attack Nantes at the end of June.

On the night of the twenty-eighth, excited by news of the imminent assault and the prospect of moving, Théophile found it difficult to sleep. He had heard about the preparations in the hospitals to receive the wounded. He had seen cannons hauled to the outskirts of the city. He had watched the erection of barricades in the streets.

Suddenly he woke up. Thunder? In the next room the silvery peal of a clock spelled three. He rose and went to the window. The moon was shining in a cloudless sky. Then he heard Uncle Guillaume: "Of course, I have to go." And a low voice he scarcely recognized as Aunt Désirée's: "Don't go now. Curfew is rigid. They'll shoot on sight. Wait until daylight or I go with you." And again Uncle Guillaume: "Your duty is with the children. Mine is at the hospital."

Their steps died in the hall. A door was closed gently. Théophile looked outside. In the deserted street he saw Uncle Guillaume walking briskly and in the silent house he heard Aunt Désirée sobbing softly. Again the rumble filled the air. War had come to Nantes.

He ran to his aunt. "I'll help you move," he said, embracing her.

Quickly she dried her eyes. "No moving today and no school. The Chouans have attacked."

All day they stayed home among trunks and bundles. At times the firing seemed nearer. At times it came from another direction. News was contradictory: the Chouans had been pushed back; the Chouans were entering the city. Uncle Guillaume managed to send a message. He had reached the hospital safely and the wounded were many.

Toward evening an orderly came with the order: "Be prepared. All hospitals are full. We are sending wounded soldiers to private homes."

In haste mattresses were thrown on the floor and the children put to work. They were to unravel handkerchiefs and napkins to make lint for dressings.

Soon the wounded were brought in. Théophile, forgotten in the excitement, watched them all evening, unaware that the sight of their suffering had planted a seed in his heart that was to shape his life.

The following morning Uncle Guillaume came home exhausted but smiling. The Chouans had been repulsed. Nantes was saved.

Nantes was saved from the Chouans but not from strife within.

CHAPTER 3

Fighting an early October storm, Théophile and Michaud arrived from school one afternoon laden with two large bundles. Théophile ran upstairs to the room where his aunt was sewing with her mother. "*Bonjour, Grandma, bonjour, Auntie.*"

"I hope you didn't catch cold in this rain," said Aunt Désirée. "I should have kept you indoors today. You coughed this morning."

Théophile hit his chest with his fist. "I'm strong," and he coughed as he spoke.

"And you always have colds. Come and get warm near the fire."

"Good marks in school?" asked Madame de Gennes, dropping her tapestry.

Théophile answered with a vague "Yes" and went back to the door. "Eh, Michaud, bring the lanterns."

"The . . . what?"

"Here they are!" and Michaud threw the two wet bundles on the floor.

"The rug!" sighed Madame de Gennes.

"Illuminations tonight," announced Théophile, "to celebrate the arrival of the new governor."

"Illuminations in this storm?"

"Government orders. We were given those lanterns at school to be sure we'd decorate the windows."

"And who is the new governor?"

"Monsieur Carrier."

"Citizen Carrier," corrected Théophile, "Michaud, shame on you. Don't you know the old title is out?"

"Oh yes," repeated Michaud, "Citizen Carrier."

"That madman?" exclaimed Madame de Gennes, "He has instigated massacres. He is responsible for the killing of the moderate members of the Convention. I hope someone has the courage to tell him he is the scourge of the earth."

"Mother!"

"My window will stay dark." And Madame de Gennes went to her room.

"We'll have to illuminate no matter what we think," concluded Aunt Désirée, "but where are the candles?"

"The school didn't give us any."

"For good reasons. They are scarce. I may not have enough."

"Cut them in two," advised Théophile, "and let's go to work."

When Uncle Guillaume came home he found everyone busy trying to keep the candles from being snuffed out by the wind. Joseph had gone out. He was a member of the reception committee.

From the library where he and Michaud were in charge of the lanterns Théophile could hear Uncle Guillaume speaking to Aunt Désirée. "Yes," he said, "I have been criticized."

"I'm sure you exaggerate."

"Unfortunately I don't. Your cousin Yves Prigent warned me not to express my opinions too freely."

"Guillaume, everybody knows you are a good republican."

"I certainly was for a change from the old regime. But how can I approve of these executions, twenty and more every day, men, women, even children, a girl of fifteen, a boy of thirteen? Have we become so weak that nobody dares speak up against such bloodshed? And now Carrier is here. He's quick at sending people to the guillotine. Only God knows what will happen."

Théophile shuddered. He had watched the condemned march to their death. Uncle Guillaume could be arrested and the whole family sent to the guillotine. "Would I be as courageous as those I saw?" was his first reaction. He

looked at Michaud. Michaud was trying to read by the dim
light and occasionally spelled a difficult word aloud.

When dinnertime came they all sat without a word.
Suddenly the silence was broken by a pistol shot and
the noise of shattered glass. Everybody started. A voice
shouted from the street, "Your windows are dark, you
Chouan dogs. That'll teach you."

Uncle Guillaume got up. "You stay here. I'll go and
light the candles again." He looked at the children. They
were white with fear, but not Théophile. He had got up
too and was clenching his fists. "How dare they break your
windows, Uncle?"

Uncle Guillaume shrugged his shoulders hopelessly.
"We should watch more carefully." And he went to attend
to the lanterns.

The following evening the family was in the parlor, waiting for supper. Christophe and Ambroise were romping
with Mirza, Michaud was teasing Jacquot, Aunt Désirée
and her mother were sewing, Uncle Guillaume was reading.
As he went to the oil lamp to turn up the wick there was a
noise outside and the door knocker fell heavily several times.
All listened to voices in the hall. "It sounds like Yves
Prigent," said Madame de Gennes, "and he is not alone."

Uncle Guillaume walked to the door with Aunt Désirée
and Théophile followed quietly.

Here was Cousin Yves Prigent with a man, an official evidently. His enormous felt tricorne was adorned with three plumes in the colors of the new flag, blue, white, and red. A gaudy uniform full of gold braid and medals made him look pompous. One of his hands was resting on the hilt of his sword and he gesticulated with the other.

Yves Prigent introduced him: "Citizen Carrier, our new governor."

The bestial face of the new governor grimaced in what he meant to be a smile. Uncle Guillaume, startled for a second, composed himself immediately and welcomed him.

"Citizen Doctor," said Carrier, rattling his sword on the floor, "I'm happy to salute you as one of the staunch defenders of the Revolution. Your wife is charming and my old friend Prigent"—and he slapped Prigent's back heartily —"told me she is a good hostess. So I came to see if he had spoken the truth."

Aunt Désirée held out her hand. "I'll be honored, Citizen Carrier, if you'll join us for supper."

"Of course, of course," said Citizen Carrier with a big laugh. "I came for that. I understand you have a fine cellar too, full of good wines. I'm ready to appreciate them."

Théophile, half hidden by his aunt's wide skirt, tried to inch his way out. He did not like the citizen governor.

Carrier saw him. "Your son? One of the defenders of the Revolution of course."

Uncle Guillaume replied: "No . . ."

Before he could continue Carrier had grabbed Théophile's arm. "You are not a defender of the Revolution?" And he made the gesture of cutting his neck.

"You misunderstood, Citizen Carrier," Aunt Désirée intervened. "My husband said no to your first question. Théophile is not our son but our nephew. I have two nephews here and two sons."

Carrier let Théophile's arm go. "Are they all good republicans?"

"They certainly are," said Aunt Désirée, vouching for the political opinions of her brood, including three-year-old Ambroise, "and so is my mother, Citizeness de Gennes."

"Guillotine the 'de,'" ordered Carrier. "It smells of nobility. That offends my republican nose."

Keeping his hat on his head, dragging his saber on the rug, Carrier was introduced to "Citizeness Gennes," who acknowledged his greeting with an icy smile. He extended his hands over the heads of the children. "My civic benediction to these defenders of the Revolution," he said with emphasis. "I dedicate them to its cult. I'm the high priest of the new religion."

As he was led into the dining room by Uncle Guillaume and "Citizeness Gennes," Aunt Désirée stayed behind with her cousin.

"Why did you bring him here?" she whispered, trembling.

"I thought it was wise to have him meet you after what had been said against Guillaume."

"I'm afraid, Yves, I'm afraid of Mother. That's all." Aunt Désirée sighed and joined her guests.

The supper progressed smoothly and Carrier was in a happy mood. After emptying several bottles of wine he declared he felt at home, threw away his hat, removed his saber, and opened the collar of his uniform. His table manners matched his language and, to the children's amusement, he used his fingers more than his fork. Michaud, encouraged by his example, grabbed a chicken wing with his hand. Théophile jabbed him with his elbow. "Michaud, your fork."

Michaud did not answer and looked at their guest. Carrier caught it. "Eat with your fingers, lad. This is the age of liberty. Everybody does as he pleases."

Aunt Désirée changed the conversation. "Now for a bottle of Muscadet. It is a wine from our province."

"Good, very good," said Carrier, smacking his lips. "It will even be better when the blood of those cursed Chouans has fertilized your hills."

There was a silence. Aunt Désirée looked at her mother. Madame de Gennes had not moved.

Carrier got up, a little unsteady on his feet. "Citizens,"

he said, lifting his glass, "I came to purify Nantes. I will shoot, I will guillotine, I will crush into a pulp the last nobles, priests, and all lukewarm republicans, and I drink to the success of my enterprise."

He sat down, swallowed another glass of Muscadet, and wiped his lips with his sleeve. He waited for compliments. It came when Madame de Gennes answered with poise, "I am afraid this is a program that only ruffians would think of carrying through."

Carrier jumped to his feet. "That old she-wolf, that Chouan female, she called me a ruffian." He pounded on the table with his fist. "Prigent, you lied to me. They are but a bunch of counterfeit republicans. They don't deserve to breathe."

Aunt Désirée tried to save the situation. She got up, a glass in her hand. "I hope you are successful with your administration," she said. "My mother did not mean to insult you, I am sure. Please have another glass of Muscadet."

Yves Prigent made him sit down. "Citizen Carrier, look at the reception my cousins gave you, their best food, their finest wines. Doesn't it prove their sympathy with your ideas?"

Uncle Guillaume had turned white and Théophile could not swallow. He felt the cold blade of the guillotine on his neck.

Carrier hesitated a moment. He gulped another glass of Muscadet and looked at Madame de Gennes. "Must be senile. Now, we'll drink to the Republic, one and indivisible."

There was nothing else to do. The shadow of the scaffold had filled the room.

After more wine and more food Carrier began to relent. He complimented Aunt Désirée on her supper and told Uncle Guillaume he would come again. He left, supported by Yves Prigent.

The family went upstairs without any comment.

"I don't like him," said Michaud to his brother when they were alone in their room.

"I don't like him either," repeated Théophile, and, throwing his pillow across the bed, he added, "And to think I was glad to put up these lanterns for him."

When the family gathered for breakfast the next morning Aunt Désirée's eyes were red and Uncle Guillaume was tense. Madame de Gennes had stayed in her room. Ambroise and Christophe sensed the anxiety that preyed on everybody. Michaud drank his hot chocolate slowly, looking at his uncle above the rim of his cup. Théophile felt a lump in his throat.

The pounding of a fist on the door startled them. Aunt Désirée ran to the hall before Uncle Guillaume could stop her. He followed quickly. Théophile went to the window.

A man in dirty rags with a stunning plumed hat was handing a letter to Aunt Désirée. He left.

Théophile breathed more easily. "He's gone. He did not arrest Uncle Guillaume." He went to the hall. Aunt Désirée was opening the letter. She looked at it and with a shrill laugh threw herself against Uncle Guillaume's shoulder. "Read," she cried, and her laughter broke into sobs.

Uncle Guillaume glanced at the paper and let it drop. He embraced Aunt Désirée. "You saved my life yesterday. I escaped the worst."

Théophile picked up the letter. It read:

The Citizen Doctor Guillaume Laennec will report to his hospital at once. He is not to leave it for the next six weeks.

Signed: Carrier

❖ CHAPTER 4

Through the end of 1793 and during the first weeks of 1794 the situation grew worse. Food was scarce, clothing could not be replaced, the newly created paper money, the *assignats,* had little if any value, and an epidemic of typhus desolated the region.

Carrier ruled Nantes as he had said he would. He came to kill and he did. Firing squads and the guillotine, which took twenty-four to twenty-seven lives daily, were active but Carrier found them too slow. He instituted mass drowning. Stripped and chained two by two, the condemned were herded into the hold of a Dutch galley anchored at the Ile Feydeau, while all night Carrier and his accomplices feasted on good food and rare wines on the upper deck. At dawn the galley sailed to the deeper Loire estuary and the victims were transferred to specially made barges. Plugs were removed from their bottoms and the barges were left to sink with their human cargo. From rafts, the executioners

watched for any survivors. They were quickly pushed under by the laughing revelers. Nantes lived in fear and
horror.

In February a wind of happiness swept over the city.
Carrier had been arrested. Reports of his cruelty had
reached the Convention, and he was taken to Paris to stand
trial. The notables of Nantes, among them Uncle Guillaume, were commanded to come and testify before the
Revolutionary Tribunal.

The doctor's absence meant no income, and Théophile
realized that he and his brother added to the hardships and
sacrifices in their uncle's family. Very little help came from
their father. Papa Laennec, now a judge at Quimperlé, sent
a rare ten-pound *assignat,* invariably accompanied by a
letter full of enthusiasm for his new social contacts with
charming ladies. Never did he express any desire to see his
children, although he referred to them as *my* Michaud,
my Théophile.

The urge to help obsessed Théophile. One day he announced to his aunt that he had a very serious problem to
discuss with her.

"Sit down, Théophile, and tell me," said Aunt Désirée,
who was darning an old stocking.

"Auntie dear, don't you think it is time I chose a career?"

"You have time, you are only thirteen."

"That's the age to do it."

"And what makes you think so?"

"My friend Bridon. He is thirteen too. He has just been admitted to the new School of Engineering, and I want to be an engineer like him."

"Ah."

Théophile could detect disapproval in her quick "Ah." He began to explain how wonderful a profession engineering was. He would graduate in three years, and he would not be a burden any more.

Aunt Désirée leaned toward him. "You are no burden," she said with affection. "We have four sons and we do our best for them. I think, in your uncle's absence, that you should write your father and ask for his advice."

"I owe him a letter. He sent us ten pounds last week." And Théophile ran to the library, sharpened a quill, and wrote:

My dear Papa,

I have received the ten pounds you kindly sent us. We needed it. If you would be so good as to allow us 100 or 150 pounds yearly it would supply our many needs, such as books, shoes, and other things. Everything is rationed, everything is expensive. My uncle earns half of what he used to and nothing at present since he had to go to Paris. If you have some old clothes you could send them to us. Aunt Désirée would mend them and adjust them to our size. She makes many a sacrifice to keep us in food and clothing.

My brother and I must think soon of choosing a profession, so
that we won't importune you any longer. Michaud will probably
go to the navy. I am attracted by engineering but I am afraid I
will not able to afford it.

I will follow your advice and my uncle's. May I ask you to answer me as soon as you have thought it over.

My brother assures you of his respectful sentiments. Kindly
accept mine.

Signed: René Théophile Laennec

While Théophile waited for an answer Aunt Désirée
exchanged letters with her husband. He was not in favor
of the School of Engineering and wrote: "Théophile has
enough judgment, even at thirteen, to understand that he
must wait and, heaven permitting, I'll soon be back among
you."

Théophile understood and accepted the idea of going
back to school, at least until he had heard from his father.
The answer was slow to come. By the time it arrived the
School of Engineering was forgotten. Théophile had
changed his mind.

When it reached him, two months later, it startled the
family. In glowing terms Théo Laennec announced that he
had married one of his clients, a charming young widow,
beautiful, intelligent, rich. At least there were hopes that
she would be when her tangled estate, seized by the Con-

vention, was restored to her. After several pages of praise for his new wife he remembered his son's letter and stated his feelings in his usual style: "My Théophile's choice of a career in engineering pleases me. As to my Michaud, I will not consent to the dangerous profession of the sea. He who created it could have had the soul of a hero; I doubt if he had the heart of a father."

Théophile continued to attend the Institution Nationale. He wrote poetry in his spare time and began to practice the flute with the diligence he gave to whatever he did. His ear was keen, his interest considerable. He soon became proficient not only at playing but at reading and writing music as well.

He never neglected his first love, botany, and used to spend one afternoon a week with the director of the Apothecaries' Garden, Monsieur Le Meignan.

This scattered activity worried his aunt. "He has too many interests and I must admit he is successful in all of them, but I'm afraid he'll become a well-educated good-for-nothing like his father."

"I don't think so," was Uncle Guillaume's invariable answer. "The boy has a serious mind. He'll know what to choose when the time comes."

"Strangely enough," she said one day, approaching the subject more directly, "he has never shown any interest in medicine. Have you asked him?"

"No, and I don't want to, perhaps because it is my dearest wish to see him become a physician. He is so sensitive, so eager to please, that he might interpret my question as a hint, take up medicine, and later regret it. Don't worry. He is only thirteen."

CHAPTER 5

U. S. 1454016

One Thursday morning (there was no school on Thursdays) Théophile was in the library practicing on his flute when the front doorbell rang. Forbidden to open if nobody was home, he kept playing. The bell rang a second time and a voice called, "We need a doctor. Please hurry!" He glanced outside. Two men were at the door. One was holding his left arm against his body and was leaning heavily on his companion. Théophile put his flute down. "Oh! He is wounded. I'll let them in." He went downstairs to meet them. "Dr. Laennec is not home," he said. "If you care to wait, I don't think my uncle will be long."

"I'll wait," said the injured man. "Walking is agony."

"And," added the other, "I would not want another doctor to touch my friend's arm. Dr. Laennec once fixed my leg when it was broken. I have faith in him. We'll wait."

The two sat in the hall. The patient did not want to speak but the other was in a talkative mood. "Are you helping your uncle?"

"No. In fact I'm not allowed even in the waiting room."

"A wonderful doctor, your uncle," continued the man. "He'll save my friend's arm as he saved my leg."

Théophile was curious. "What happened to your friend?"

"He lost his balance while climbing on a high ladder, tried to catch himself on a rung with his left arm, and fell all the way to the ground. Now his left arm is paralyzed."

"Must be a fracture," said Théophile.

The injured man spoke. "It is wonderful to be a doctor but it takes a stout heart."

Théophile did not answer. Uncle Guillaume was entering.

"Uncle, these men want to see you. I told them to wait."

"Very well. I'll take them to my office."

Théophile went back to the library, left the door ajar, and listened.

From the office came a few grunts, even a cry of pain.

Suddenly Uncle Guillaume called, "Théophile!" He was pushing the friend of the injured man out of the room. "Théophile, take care of him. Fetch a glass of cognac. He's ready to faint."

Théophile looked at the man. His face, deadly white, was covered with beads of perspiration. Stumbling on his feet, he mumbled, "Can't see anyone suffer."

"I understand," replied Uncle Guillaume. "Sit down and put your head low between your knees. You'll be all right in a minute. Théophile, he's your patient."

Théophile ran to the dining room. The liquor closet was locked. He rushed back to his patient and found him on the floor in a dead faint. Although he knew he should not disturb his uncle when he was busy, he realized this was urgent and he knocked at the office door with decision.

"Come in."

Théophile entered and saw the patient lying on the floor. Uncle Guillaume's foot was on the armpit, and he was stretching the injured arm. "What is it?" he asked without turning his head.

"My patient has fainted," explained Théophile, "and the liquor closet is locked."

"Leave him where he is. I'll attend to him after I've reduced this luxation." And to the patient: "Have courage. It's only a dislocated shoulder and I'll replace it in no time. It'll be painful but it won't last."

"Go ahead, Doctor," the man said, biting his lips.

Uncle Guillaume braced himself, maintained his weight on the armpit, extended the arm, rotated it. The man gave one scream. The shoulder had snapped into place.

Théophile had not moved. He had joined his hands in awe, and admiration showed on his face.

Uncle Guillaume noticed him. "You are still here,

Théophile? Now let's take care of the other. Here is the key to the liquor closet. Get two glasses of cognac. They both need a little stimulant."

Théophile came back holding the two glasses firmly. His hands were not trembling. Uncle Guillaume observed him from the corner of his eyes while bandaging his patient's arm.

Théophile was helping "his" patient to sit up. He held the glass for him and asked, "Do you feel better now?"

"I do," the man said after taking a sip. "My friend was right. You need a stout heart to be a doctor. I could never be one. Could you?" And, without waiting for an answer: "Of course you could. You didn't flinch."

When they were ready to leave, the patient put his hand in his pocket. "I don't have much, Doctor, but all I have is yours. My arm is as good as new."

"Didn't I tell you Dr. Laennec is the best surgeon in the whole city?" said the other, who had recovered his strength.

Uncle Guillaume laughed frankly. "Lots of doctors could have reduced your luxation. I don't want any money. I've been paid for all I did."

The two men looked at each other. "I didn't give you anything," said the friend. "What do you mean?"

"Well . . ." began Uncle Guillaume. "It would take too long to explain. Go and forget it."

"God bless you, Doctor."

Uncle Guillaume closed the door and looked at Théophile. "Did you get frightened when you saw me reduce this dislocation?"

"No," said Théophile, "I knew it had to be done, no matter how painful." And he added, laughing, "I could not afford to faint either. I had to take care of the other. May I go back to my flute?"

Uncle Guillaume nodded. His eyes followed the small boy with emotion. He stepped forward as if he wanted to call him back but he stopped and went to his office.

The episode seemed forgotten. Neither of the two ever mentioned it again.

A few evenings later the family was in the parlor. Uncle Guillaume was reading. Madame de Gennes was working at her eternal tapestry. Aunt Désirée was building a fire and Mirza, alone in a corner, looked resentful at being neglected. Christophe and Michaud were blowing up their chests and measuring them with a piece of rope.

"I'm bigger than you," said Christophe, filling up his lungs.

"No, I am. Give me that rope," insisted Michaud.

Théophile was watching them. He too breathed deeply, his hands on the sides of his chest. Quietly he went to his uncle. "Uncle, may I ask you a question?"

Uncle Guillaume put his book down.

"Uncle, what makes the chest bigger when I fill it with air? I thought the chest was a cage of bones, and bones are stiff."

Uncle Guillaume smiled broadly. "It is very simple. The ribs are hinged at both ends, front and back. As the front bone, which is called the sternum, moves forward, the ribs follow. They are rigid, you are right, but they overcome the difficulty by rolling on themselves so the capacity of the cage is increased. Try to do it with your arms. Fold your hands on your sternum, let your elbows drop, now raise them. That's exactly what the ribs do. While the chest expands in front as the sternum goes forward, it expands laterally with the rolling of the ribs."

Théophile tried it several times. "It's a wonderful invention."

"The whole body is a wonderful invention."

"Uncle, tell me more about it."

"Not today. Go and play with Mirza. He looks lonesome."

Théophile obeyed. He put his hands around the dog. "Your ribs move," he said. "Your body is a wonderful machine too."

A few weeks later, after supper, Théophile was alone in the library, his favorite room. He loved its peaceful atmosphere, especially at night when the oil lamp cast a soft glow on the book-lined walls. He was so absorbed in an old leather-bound book that he did not hear someone pushing the door. It was Uncle Guillaume. He came in quietly and leaned over his nephew's shoulder. "Théophile, I did not know you were interested in Hippocrates' writings."

Théophile, surprised, replied, "Yes . . . No . . ." and, his hand on the book as if taking a solemn vow: "I want to be a physician, like you, Uncle."

Uncle Guillaume straightened up so that Théophile could not see the joy in his eyes and waited.

Théophile closed the book and, looking ahead, he spoke slowly. "It must be wonderful to cure people, to know how the human body works and what makes it get sick."

Still Uncle Guillaume did not speak. He observed the fourteen-year-old boy before him, frail, small for his age, and wondered at the determination with which he had said, "I want to be a physician."

Afraid his uncle had not taken him seriously, Théophile repeated, "It is true, Uncle, I have decided to be a physician."

"It is a hard profession, often a deceiving one. You think of success but have you realized that many times we fail to heal or even help a patient? It is heartbreaking. We must admit we don't know and it is the most difficult thing to face."

Théophile got up. He tried to understand his uncle's

attitude. "Why are you discouraging me? Don't you want me to be a physician?"

"Don't I want you to?" Uncle Guillaume's voice had changed from a deep tone to a jubilant cry. He put his hands on his nephew's shoulders and, looking intently into his gray eyes, repeated slowly, "Don't I want you to?"

"Then why didn't you encourage me sooner in that direction?"

"Medicine is a vocation. I have often wished you would hear the call but I never would have exerted any pressure one way or the other. As I said, one is called to be a physician. If you heed that call you are embracing a richly rewarding career, full of pitfalls, full of deceptions, full of sacrifices, but full of happiness. You feel you are approaching the secrets of nature and people look up to you for help. You can't always help them, but your conscience tells you you have done your best and that is what counts. Théophile, you make me very happy."

The following day, at breakfast, there was happiness in the air. Uncle Guillaume exchanged smiles with Aunt Désirée and Jacquot shrieked more loudly than ever before.

Théophile alone was serious. He felt he had grown up overnight.

At the end of the meal Uncle Guillaume addressed Théophile. "Thursday today, no school. What would you say if I asked you to make rounds with me?"

Théophile's face reflected surprise, his eyes sparkled, he opened his mouth but could not find the words to express his feelings.

Michaud giggled. "Dr. René Théophile Laennec is going to visit his patients. The Lord have mercy on them."

Everybody laughed except Théophile. He jabbed his brother with his elbow and said, "I'll go with you, Uncle." And he was at the door before his uncle.

The two left the house on foot. These were hard times and many months ago the horse and buggy had been sold.

"Théophile," said Uncle Guillaume, "we are going to the Hôtel-Dieu, I mean the Temple de l'Humanité. Can't get used to that new name. I want to show you the rugged side of medicine. As for attending a medical school, we have no medical school anywhere in France. The Convention has closed all universities under the pretext of reorganizing them. Who knows when they'll reopen? But with two of my friends we'll hold private classes in September. In the meantime you'll make rounds with me and I'll teach you the rudiments of anatomy."

The distance was short and they soon reached the Hôtel-Dieu. The old name had been scratched out and a crudely chiseled "Temple de l'Humanité" replaced it. It was a dismal building with iron grillwork on the windows.

To evaluate medicine at the end of the eighteenth century, one must remember that it had not progressed much

since the time of Hippocrates, about 400 B.C. All over the
world—and France was no exception—epidemics raged
without check. The causes of symptoms were not investi-
gated. If the symptoms were not described in the writings
of Galen or Hippocrates, the patient was wrong, not *the
book*. Fevers were treated with preparations "to cool the
blood," swellings with ointments of frogs' eyes or rats'
livers. The most universal remedy was bloodletting "to
draw the bad humors out." Lancets or leeches were used in
the process.

And no one would have thought that the little boy entering the "Temple de l'Humanité" was to be instrumental
in opening a new era.

As they entered the wide arched door they heard the
steps of a horse and had to stand against the wall to let a
hearse go by. Théophile looked at his uncle and said nothing. They kept going, pushed a gate, and were in the
courtyard. In the center, hens were searching for food in a
heap of refuse. At the sight of the visitors they cackled and
flew awkwardly in all directions, to return to their foraging
as soon as danger was gone.

"This way," said Uncle Guillaume to Théophile, who
had stopped to inspect the surroundings. They came to
another building, climbed two flights of stairs, and arrived
at a large room. It was a men's ward. Fourteen beds on
one side, fourteen on the other, each screened with white

curtains. All were drawn open except one. At the other end of the ward a group of men made a gesture of welcome when they saw Dr. Laennec. He walked rapidly toward them. Théophile hesitated a moment. The shut-in bed attracted his attention. From under the curtain rose a panting respiration interrupted by spells of hacking coughing. He had stopped and looked at the drawn curtains as if trying to guess their secret, then walked back of his uncle.

"Here is my nephew," announced Uncle Guillaume, "one of your future students, Bacque."

The man, who had a large white apron around his waist, held out his hand. "You want to join the disciples of Hippocrates?"

Without embarrassment, Théophile answered, "With your help, sir, and my uncle's encouragement."

"Where is Darbefeuille?" asked Uncle Guillaume.

"In the autopsy room. Number 6 died yesterday and he wants to find out if his diagnosis was right."

"Very well, I'll go and see him. Come with me, Théophile."

They went downstairs to the autopsy room. There were no windows, it was dark. In the center, lit by candles which projected grotesque shadows on the walls, was a slab with a lifeless body. Théophile felt dizzy. The stench was almost unbearable. "I must not weaken," he thought, "or they'll laugh at me."

"Darbefeuille, this is my nephew. He'll join your class in the fall."

"I'll be glad to have you with me," said Dr. Darbefeuille, and to Dr. Laennec: "This is Number 6, remember him? Pus all over his lungs. Phthisis, one of the many kinds of phthisis. Laennec, I can describe seventeen or eighteen kinds of phthisis. Sometimes I find cavities in the lungs, sometimes small nodules, millions of them, sometimes pus, as in this case."

"How is Bed 11?"

"The end."

"I thought so. His bed was closed."

Number 11 . . . that was the bed that had attracted Théophile. He understood. Misery might be exposed, but the last breath of a dying man was sheltered from indifferent eyes. A great desire to learn overwhelmed his disgust, but he felt dizzy. He put his hand on his uncle's arm. Uncle Guillaume noticed his pallor. "I think we'd better go. Your initiation has been a hard one."

They went back to the courtyard. Théophile welcomed the daylight. Fresh air had never felt fresher to him. They walked past the cackling hens and Uncle Guillaume concluded, "Go home now. I have to make rounds at the army hospital."

Théophile answered in a clear voice, "May I go with you?"

↭ CHAPTER 6

Summer should have been vacation time, but Théophile thought differently.

As soon as school was over he organized his free hours to complete certain gaps in his education. His knowledge of physics and chemistry was deficient. It had to be remedied. Latin he knew well but Greek had been omitted from his programs. A distinguished Hellenist, Father Bonnement, was chosen to be his teacher. He continued to study music and, to everybody's surprise, started dancing lessons.

These many activities did not distract him from what he now considered his life's aim. He spent hours in the library reading medical books until Uncle Guillaume stopped him. "You are not ready yet," he said. "You have to begin from the beginning, and here is what you need." And he handed Théophile a long wooden box.

Théophile opened it. "A skeleton!"

"And a treatise on osteology, the science of the bones. When you can name on sight any of the two hundred-odd bones of the human body and describe it correctly, you are ready for further studies."

Théophile took the box to his room and that evening, under the dim light of a candle and against Aunt Désirée's order to go to bed at once, he looked at the bones, read their descriptions, marveled at their shapes, till sleep overcame him.

In the morning he was late for breakfast. "I'll straighten my room later," he thought.

Uncle Guillaume had already left and Aunt Désirée was eating with the children. A scream startled them. "It's Corentine, the new maid. What happened?" said Aunt Désirée, running out.

Théophile giggled. He had an idea what had happened.

At the top of the stairs Corentine, pale, her eyes filled with fear, was sobbing hysterically. "Don't go in," she begged, panting, "There is a ghost in Master Théophile's bedroom."

Théophile answered coldly, "It is my skeleton, to study osteology."

"Yes, a skeleton," repeated Corentine, crossing herself. "You should have him buried in holy ground."

Aunt Désirée pushed the door open. There was a femur on a chair, a hand was dangling from the key of the dresser, and a skull lay on the desk. "Théophile," she said, repressing a laugh, "please put these bones in their box and be sure they stay there."

"Even with the box closed, madame, I'll never clean this room."

And she kept her word.

Soon the skeleton held no secret from Théophile.

"What is this?" Uncle Guillaume would ask. "And this?"

At first there had been some hesitation, some mistakes, but after a while there were none. As a reward Théophile was sent twice a week to the Hôpital de la Paix, an army center of which Uncle Guillaume was chief surgeon.

Rest was unknown to Théophile, and he soon was to pay for this intense activity. Chills and fever seized him. He was ordered to bed and obeyed, or at least pretended to. He used to wait until everybody was asleep before lighting a candle he had saved for that purpose and reading a good part of the night.

In September came the day he had awaited with eagerness, his first day as a medical student. It was a clear cool morning and he ran all the way to the Hôtel-Dieu. Near the building he slowed his pace. "A medical student should exhibit poise," he thought. Still he could not resist the fun of shooing away the cackling hens foraging in the refuse. He went to Dr. Bacque's office as he had been told to do. It was a tiny room on the ground floor. Near the window

an easel supported a large blackboard. In the center was a
desk on a small platform and, scattered around, some desks
for the students. Three of them were already seated when
Théophile entered. Instead of Dr. Bacque, a younger man
was occupying the teacher's desk. He greeted Théophile's
arrival with a nod and showed him a seat.

The students observed Théophile with curiosity. One of
them said, "You are Dr. Laennec's nephew, aren't you?"
And with a touch of surprise: "You are awfully young.
How old are you?"

"Fourteen."

"That old? I thought you were twelve."

It was true. Théophile appeared younger than he was.
He did not like the comment about his age and chose not
to answer.

"He's a snob," mumbled another student. "All he'll
have to do is to live on his uncle's reputation."

"At that age, what will he know? He's a baby."

Before more whispers could be exchanged, Dr. Bacque
entered. He uttered a brief "Good morning" and addressed
his colleague: "Desray, I thought we were expecting five
students. Where is the fifth one?"

"Here I am," and a fat boy rushed in. "I had to help
my father open his store."

Dr. Desray had stepped off the platform but Dr. Bacque
did not take his place. He walked back and forth, rubbed

his hands, and began: "I welcome you on your first day as
medical students. Dr. Desray will be in charge of the dissection class. I must see if you are ready for it. The back-
bone of anatomy being osteology, the science of the bones"
—and Dr. Bacque smiled at his own pun—"I want to find
out how much you know of it."

He opened a drawer, took a triangular bone, held it at
arm's length. "What is it?"

All hands went up.

"Let's start with the first desk. Describe it."

The student who had questioned Théophile got up, took
the bone in his hands. "It is a scapula, sir."

"Very good. Left or right?"

The student put the bone over his right shoulder, then
over the left one in an awkward gesture that made the
others laugh. "A left scapula, sir."

"Go on."

"Eh . . . it is a triangular bone . . . eh . . . It
goes in the back . . . eh . . . That piece that sticks out
is the . . . the . . . eh . . ."

"Next desk."

The next desk was Théophile's. "It is called the
acromion."

"Oh yes," said the student, "the acromion. It helps
form the shoulder." A silence. Apparently that was all he
knew.

"Laennec, can you describe it a little more scientifically?"

Théophile got up. Holding the scapula in his left hand, he illustrated his description with his right index finger, following the edges as he spoke. "Three borders, superior, vertebral, and axillary. Two surfaces, one anterior, one posterior."

The students looked at each other. "The baby knows something."

Sitting near Théophile was the late-comer. He showed increasing fright as his turn was approaching.

"Did you study the skull?"

"Yes, sir."

"How many bones in the cranium?"

"Eight."

"In the face?"

"Fourteen."

"What is this?"

"A sphenoid, sir, a bone from inside the skull."

"Describe it."

"It has been compared to a bird because it has four wings."

"Good. But to your knowledge, what bird has four wings?"

The fat student blushed. He looked at the queerly shaped bone, he looked at the ceiling, his lips moved, but no sound came out.

Théophile felt sorry for him. He tried to prompt him when Dr. Bacque turned away to take another bone from the drawer: "A b . . ." The boy nodded. He had understood. Triumphantly he exclaimed, "A butterfly."

A burst of laughter greeted his words. Even Dr. Bacque joined in the mirth. "You are almost right," he said when the uproar had subsided. "It begins with a *b*. The correct answer should have been a bat, not a butterfly. Let's continue."

The last two did fairly well, one with a calcaneus, the bone of the heel; the other with a vertebra from the neck, the atlas. Whenever they did not know, Théophile had the correct answer.

Amused and interested by his youngest student, Dr. Bacque threw a small bone on Théophile's desk. "Do you know this one?"

Théophile turned it in his hands for a second. "It is one of the eight bones of the wrist, the scaphoid, also called os naviculare. May I have the other wristbones, sir? I'll assemble them."

His deft fingers picked them up without hesitation and the two wrists were reconstructed to the admiration of the class.

Dr. Bacque concluded, "I give you another week to master osteology and I expect the four of you to be able to compete with Laennec. However, I don't want to delay the opening of the dissection class. Be here tomorrow at eight. You may go."

When Théophile arrived home he found a letter from his stepmother. She was happy to announce that they had returned to Quimper and had taken back Marie-Anne, and Michaud was invited to come and live with them. As for Théophile, she understood he had to remain at Nantes for his medical education. Without picking up the three-hundred-pound *assignat* that had fallen from the letter, Théophile said with tears in his eyes, "Michaud . . . that means we'll be separated."

Aunt Désirée tried to comfort him. "Not right away, and you could go and visit them later on."

Théophile shook his head. "And I was so happy today, my first day as a medical student."

Day after day the rigid schedule was maintained. Dissection from eight to ten, then rounds at the Hôtel-Dieu and homework in the afternoon. Théophile seemed to thrive on it. His health improved; he was full of enthusiasm and he was happy. Michaud was still with them. He was not to leave for Quimper until after the first of the year.

At the beginning of December, Uncle Guillaume informed Théophile of his appointment at the Hôpital de la Paix as a third-class health officer, and with a salary.

Théophile could have jumped to the ceiling. He cer-

tainly had not expected it, he, a first-year medical student
and not yet fifteen. Feeling the importance of his new position, he remarked, "I hope nobody takes me for twelve years
old."

The following day he reported to the Hôpital de la Paix.
"So, you are the new health officer?" was the only comment
of his colleagues. Théophile felt better. He was shown his
ward and was told to take the case history of a new patient.
He approached the bed and in his most professional manner
began his inquiry.

First question: "How old are you?" and he thought,
"Funny that I should be asking this."

The patient answered in Breton, "I don't speak French."

This did not embarrass Théophile. He had a fair knowl
edge of the idiom of his province, the old Celtic tongue
common to Wales and Brittany.

Second question: "What's the trouble?"

The man showed his leg. A deep sore had eaten away
the flesh along the shin, exposing the diseased bone.

"How long have you had this?"

"At times it heals, at times it comes back."

"And that? How long have you had that?" Théophile
had noticed a swelling in the groin on the same side.

"Every time the sore appears, there it is."

Théophile made a note of it and continued his examination. He was ready when Uncle Guillaume appeared with

several doctors. They gathered around the bed of the new patient and Théophile was told to present the case. He did it in a clear and concise manner, barely consulting his notes, and concluded, "The fact that there is a swollen gland in the groin every time the ulcer opens gives me the impression the two are related."

Uncle Guillaume nodded approvingly. One of the doctors asked Théophile, "Anyone helped you?"

"No, sir."

"Young man, I want to congratulate you on the intelligent manner with which you took this history. It shows a sense of observation. You are right, the sore and the swelling are related. This man has an inflammation of the tibia and the reaction from the gland is the rule in such cases. Guillaume, what do you think of your nephew?"

"I am extremely pleased and not surprised. I knew he'd do well."

Patting Théophile on the shoulder, another asked, "How old are you?"

The dreaded question! Théophile stiffened up, hesitated, and said, "I'll be fifteen shortly." Fifteen in the future sounded better than fourteen in the present.

"Keep on, Laennec. I'm sure you'll go far in the profession you have chosen."

❦ CHAPTER 7

Work, work, and more work. So ended 1795 for Théophile and so began 1796, a year which presaged great changes.

A new government, the Directoire, had replaced the blood-soaked Convention, and before the five Directeurs lay the gigantic task of reorganizing the country.

In Uncle Guillaume's house life continued as before, except for Michaud's absence. At the beginning of the year he had gone to live with his father and the new Madame Laennec. The saddened Théophile planned to visit them when his finances permitted, but by the next year the military hospitals were closed and the commissions abolished following the end of the Chouans' revolt. Undecided about what to do, he was tempted to sign up as surgeon on a corsair ship, but a letter from his stepmother made him change his mind. She invited him to come and live with them at Quimper, at least for a few months.

Théophile wrote at once to his father, asking him to help pay for the trip.

The money came, and in July he took a boat for Lorient. The rest of the way he walked, a matter of forty miles, and how he enjoyed the scenery! Yellow blossoms dotted the spiky bushes of thornbroom on the low walls bordering the fields. In the valleys the golden wheat and the rye were already announcing the harvest season.

It took him three days to reach Quimper. Quimper, where he was born, Quimper, the heart of Brittany. It was drizzling as it had the day Uncle Michel brought him and Michaud to their father's home. There he stood before the door, remembering how he had had to stand on his toes to reach the brass knocker. Today he did not need to. He was sixteen.

The knocker fell back with the sound he knew so well and Maria opened the door. While they embraced a young girl came running. "Good day, big brother. I'm Marie-Anne." And Michaud slid down the banister and tumbled on them. In the confusion they had not seen a pretty woman, dressed in the newest fashion, at the top of the stairs. She came down swiftly and opened her arms. "My big son, I welcome you with all my heart. Now my family is complete. And, please, call me Mother."

"She is nice," thought Théophile, "I knew I'd like her."

He responded to her affectionate kiss and asked about his
father.

"Your father, unfortunately, is detained at St. Brieuc for
a trial. I don't know when he'll be back."

Théophile was disappointed but the joy of being re-
united with his brother and sister overshadowed everything
else. Full of youthful exuberance, he refused to rest and
joined the family in the parlor.

A young woman greeted him. "Don't you remember
me? I'm your cousin."

"You are Madame de Pompery?"

"Cousin Anne—Annick in Breton, as I'm sure you
know."

At once Théophile felt attracted, and the attraction became admiration when his stepmother spoke of her musical
talent. "She has a pianoforte, the only one in Quimper,
and she plays the harp also."

"I've brought my flute," exclaimed Théophile. "We'll
play duets. When do we begin?"

"Not today, please, Annick," interrupted Madame
Laennec. "I want to get acquainted with my big son first.
Théophile, tell us about your trip from Nantes." And
Théophile related his adventures to the amazement of the
two women.

"And you walked?"

"He loves to walk," said Michaud.

"And you did not stop at the inns?"

"I had not enough money. My passage from Nantes to Lorient took most of the twenty pounds you so kindly sent me."

"Say francs, not pounds," laughed Michaud. "Don't you know the new name for our money?"

Madame Laennec seemed surprised. "Your uncle did not give you anything when you left?"

"He could not. His situation is not what it used to be."

Turning to Madame de Pompery, Madame Laennec declared: "Exactly what I always told you, Annick. Medicine does not feed its disciples." And to Théophile: "You really want to be a physician?"

"I do," answered Théophile firmly.

"After what you have seen? It will bring you slavery, a few thanks maybe, and no money for your old age."

Théophile's face hardened. To him, medicine was *the* profession. He could not bear to hear it belittled.

Madame Laennec continued, "We had other dreams for you, your father and I. We were hoping that commerce would attract you. Are you sure you could not become a great merchant like my grandfather?"

Théophile laughed. "I don't think I'd be good at selling anything, and I love what I'm doing."

Madame Laennec shrugged her shoulders and Cousin Annick adroitly changed the conversation.

Still, the subject of medicine was to come between them more than once, and Théophile heard again and again of the advantages of business over medicine.

After three weeks, lonely for his father, Théophile decided to go and see him at St. Brieuc, or rather Port-Brieuc, as it had been renamed by the Convention. Port-Brieuc, on the north shore of Brittany, was seventy-five miles from Quimper. He planned to walk, as usual.

This trip took him through the most beautiful part of Brittany: thick forests, rivers running between high cliffs covered with foliage and flowers among granite boulders. He felt the poetry of a region so different from the misty moors of the coast. He came across large stones erected centuries ago, the menhirs of an unknown past when the druids cut the sacred mistletoe with gold scythes. And everyday life interested him also. He talked to women washing clothes in the brooks; he watched clogmakers in the forests, potters molding clay on their lathes. He stopped at roadside farms and enjoyed tales of ghosts and *korrigans*, those elfin beings that populated forests and moors. He was a Breton, a true Celt, and he loved Brittany.

Ten days later he arrived at St. Brieuc. It was late in the day, and he lost his way. When he finally found his father's

house nobody answered his repeated knocks. As he raised
his head to see if there was any light in the upper windows,
a passer-by spoke to him. "You are looking for Monsieur
Laennec? You'll find him at the Café de la Justice, Rue
St. Guillaume. The servants are aware of their master's
habit. He never is home before the wee hours of the morning and neither are they."

With a sigh, Théophile took his bags again and went
looking for the Rue St. Guillaume. At the café he found
his father standing on a chair, orating, to the applause of a
jolly crowd. He approached without being seen, clapped
his hands, and said, "Bravo, Papa."

Papa Laennec jumped from his chair. "My Théophile!"
Taking a theatrical pose, he announced: "Gentlemen, my
elder son, the pride of my life."

Shouts of welcome greeted the presentation.

"I surmise you had a pleasant trip," said Papa Laennec,
and without waiting for the answer, "Son, you arrived here
when we were holding a celebration in honor of the new
name of this café. It will be known as the Café du Commerce from now on. Here is a bit of poetry I wrote for the
occasion." And Papa Laennec climbed on the chair again
and declaimed a short ditty. The last line, coming from a
lawyer, surprised Théophile: "No change. Justice has always been a commerce."

"Not worthy of you, Papa."

"By Jove, the subject could not inspire an epic."

And the party continued, as predicted, till the wee hours of the morning. Théophile and Papa Laennec, a lantern in his hands, walked home through St. Brieuc's dark streets.

"Well, son, how do you like my friends?"

"I like them," said Théophile earnestly. Then came a thought. His father had spoken of his talents as a poet, a Latinist, a musician, and nothing had been mentioned about medicine. He felt guilty.

"Papa, Uncle Guillaume is satisfied with my progress in medicine."

Papa Laennec stopped short. "That's right. You are a medical student." He lifted his lantern. "A queer profession. Work, no pay, no fun."

Théophile replied timidly, "It is fascinating," but the words did not ring true. The studious medical student he had been was another person. Tonight he was somebody else.

ᘓ CHAPTER 8

From that day invitation succeeded invitation. Théophile's gaiety and talent as a musician and as a dancing partner won him a well-deserved popularity.

At the end of August there was a wedding in the family. A cousin's cousin was to be married at Binic, a day's trip from St. Brieuc. The ceremony was planned for midnight, the usual time in that era.

Early in the evening the house guests, including the two Laennecs, assembled in the hall of the bride's home. Théophile noticed that Nicolette, the fiancée, kept looking at the door. "It must be love," he thought, "she can scarcely wait." Suddenly, in the middle of a conversation, she ran away with her bridesmaids. The groom had appeared. He was immediately surrounded by a crowd of singing boys and girls. "What do you want? We have nothing to sell."

"If you came for some eggs," chanted one, "we have no hens."

"If you want some bread," sang another, "the baker is sick."

Interested, Théophile took a piece of paper out of his pocket and rapidly drew some lines. He was so absorbed that he did not pay attention to people looking over his shoulder. "Ohs" and "Ahs" made him raise his head. "Shhh," he said, "I'm jotting down this melody. It is charming."

"If you want some cider," continued the chorus, "our apples rotted on the tree."

"I want Nicolette," said the groom, forcing his way inside.

Then began a chase all over the dark house, ending in the attic where the girls were hiding.

Near midnight, the grand march got under way through the village, preceded by torchbearers and bagpipers with their *binious*, akin to the Irish bagpipes.

The midnight ceremony was followed by a supper and dancing to the shrill music of the *binious*. After the native square dances, some guests asked for a minuet or a gavotte. The bagpipers did not know any. Théophile went to his room, took out his flute, and replaced the musicians, to the delight of the dancers.

In September, at the onset of the hunting season, Papa Laennec presented Théophile with a gun which he received with great pleasure; and father and son roamed the moors, shooting birds and hares.

"I'm a man of the outdoors," Théophile used to repeat, coming home, his pouch bulging with game. "I never feel better than after walking a whole day, no matter what the weather."

Many evenings were spent at the Café du Commerce but Théophile preferred to be alone with his father. He loved to stretch his legs before a roaring fire at the end of the day. "Ah, *la bonne vie,* Papa, I wish it would last."

From afar Uncle Guillaume became aware of a change in his nephew. Théophile, usually a reliable correspondent, seldom wrote. When he did, it was only to tell about the pleasant time he was having. In the fall he announced that he was returning to Quimper with his father. This prompted Uncle Guillaume to act. He asked a friend, Monsieur Crucy, a naval architect, on his way to Brest, to stop at St. Brieuc. Monsieur Crucy understood the problem and agreed to try to influence Théophile.

He was received most cordially by the Laennecs and his invitation to Théophile to go to Brest with him was met with joyous approval. The same day they left by coach.

Brest interested Théophile. He visited its deep-sea port, the arsenal, the dockyards. Monsieur Crucy said nothing about his mission.

Two days before leaving Brest, he remembered, or seemed to remember, a forgotten message. "Your uncle asked me to see someone but I have to return to the dockyards today. Why don't you go alone? He is chief surgeon of the navy hospital."

Théophile went, and that same evening he opened his heart to Monsieur Crucy. "Something gripped me as soon as I entered the hospital. It awoke a feeling that I did not know was in me. Above all, I'm a physician."

Monsieur Crucy's intervention had not been in vain.

Théophile returned to Quimper and announced that he was going back to Nantes, to the disappointment of the family. Papa Laennec spoke of the ingratitude of children and Madame Laennec was resentful. Marie-Anne and Michaud begged him to stay. Gently but firmly, Théophile stood by his decision and on October 25, 1797, after walking a hundred miles in four days, he was back at Nantes.

In November a third son was born to Aunt Désirée. He was given the Breton name of Mériadec. And life continued as in the past.

Although much absorbed by his medical studies, Théophile was still interested in music, dancing, writing poetry. He even took painting lessons, although he never showed any particular aptitude. Never idle, he could not keep up such activity and in May 1798 he became ill. He had chills, violent pains in the chest, digestive troubles. He recuperated slowly and incompletely but refused to rest when he heard that in a year a competition was to be held that could reinstate him as a health officer. He had to prepare for it. He wanted so much to earn a salary.

He passed the examination in the spring of 1799, but the expected appointment did not follow. He was told it would come at a still undetermined date. This gave him time for a vacation—and vacation meant going back to his father to relive the pleasant hours of two summers ago.

Uncle Guillaume encouraged him to go, because he had begun to think of sending Théophile to Paris to complete his medical education. A visit with his father might induce Papa Laennec to finance the undertaking.

Théophile left in August, not for Quimper but for St. Brieuc, where his father was trying to untangle his wife's estate, which had been partially confiscated by the government. He found his father, as always, writing verses, this time in praise of the Celtic mustard, a product with which a local pharmacist sought to encourage his clients' appetite.

In his enjoyment of *la bonne vie,* Théophile almost stayed longer than he had intended. In October he returned to Nantes in his usual manner, on foot. At the gates of the city he was robbed, but this was trifling compared with the news he brought. Papa Laennec had refused to subsidize the trip to Paris and Uncle Guillaume could not afford that added responsibility. So Théophile went back to the Hôtel-Dieu, hoping his reappointment as health officer would not be delayed too long.

The new century saw General Bonaparte's rise. As First Consul, he decided to quell the Chouans, who had recently been reorganized. With this state of emergency came Théophile's coveted reappointment, and he was ordered to join the army.

When he left Nantes he had only enough money to buy part of a uniform and chose to spend his last francs on a bicorne hat. He hoped it would make a favorable impression on his subordinates until he could afford more.

After going through devastated villages and looted towns, the army reached Vannes, which had not been touched by the war. Théophile was exploring the city, hoping to complete his uniform, when he met Joseph, his uncle's ex-servant, arrayed in a splendid outfit. His head was adorned with a large plumed hat, his sleeves covered with gold braid. Joseph described himself as holding a high rank in the army and, with a touch of condescension, offered his services to Théophile. Hearing of the boy's unsuccessful search, Joseph sent him to a shop in the Rue des Orfèvres. Thanks to him, Théophile found what his rank demanded, or at least part of it: collar and cuffs with gold braid, brass buttons, and a sword. And now to the battlefields! Alas, he was commanded to stay at Vannes, where he had nothing

to do. Like any idle, lonesome soldier, he deplored his in-
activity. His flute had been left at home, there were no
books around, and he knew nobody in town. But his cre-
ative mind was soon to find a diversion.

One evening, under the sputtering flame of a candle,
the idea of writing a satire on the Chouan war came to his
mind. Linking it to antiquity, he imagined that a lost Greek
poem, *La Guerre des Vénètes* (*The War of the Vénètes*),
had been discovered and translated by the "famous Dr.
Cenneal," a pen name that deceived nobody. No more
lonely hours walking aimlessly; Théophile spent his days
with the Vénètes and his evenings telling his amused companions of their valorous exploits.

The insurrection did not last long and as soon as peace
was restored the army commissions were abolished. Once
more Théophile was left without a salary. His plan to go
to Paris was fading away. He wrote his father asking for
help. Uncle Guillaume sent letter after letter but Papa
Laennec continued to give much advice and no money. His
reason? He was sending Michaud to Paris "to broaden his
mind." Although he was not jealous of his brother, Théophile was hurt and his health was affected. Digestive
troubles, headaches, mental depression put him to bed for
a couple of weeks. Finally, after much pressure, Papa Laennec promised to give Théophile a small monthly allowance.
At once Théophile was better, and on April 20, 1801, he

bade *au revoir* to those who had brought him up as their son.

For the last time he looked at the familiar surroundings, and the memory of his arrival thirteen years ago surged in his mind. He remembered the affection that greeted him, Mirza barking joyously, Jacquot screaming his *"bon . . . bonjour."* Overcome by his emotion, he left the house quickly and, without looking back, climbed into the farmer's carriage that was to take him to Angers.

▣ CHAPTER 9

The trip to Angers was uneventful. From there on Théophile resorted to his usual mode of transportation and walked the seventy-mile stretch to Orléans. He arrived tired and feverish, and could not foster enough energy to walk the rest of the way. He inquired. The stagecoach was beyond his means and he was fortunate to find a farmer who agreed to take him. Two days later, seated among cauliflowers, onions, and potatoes, Théophile entered Paris.

The city did not impress him. The gutters were littered, the houses dilapidated. On the walls the bold motto of the Revolution recalled the dark days of the Terreur: *Liberté, Egalité, Fraternité ou la Mort.*

Afraid his young companion would get lost, the farmer drove to the street where Michaud resided. When he saw the house, Théophile hesitated. It gave him a strange feeling of loneliness and poverty. He entered the dark hall. A fat, unkempt woman, the all-powerful concierge, was sweeping the stairs in a cloud of dust.

"Monsieur Laennec, please."

The woman pushed away the strands of hair that obscured her vision and examined the stranger with an insolent gaze. *"Au quatrième,"* was her curt answer.

Coughing, panting, Théophile climbed four flights. He did not feel lost any more and the unpleasant surroundings took on a different appearance. He had found his brother.

The two were truly happy to be together again. After exchanging questions and answers about the family, the trip, life in Paris, Michaud explained that he had enrolled at the university, now the Ecole Centrale des Quatre Nations.

Théophile laid out his plan. He was going to register at the Ecole de Santé, which had replaced the old School of Medicine. "And I'll attend rounds in a hospital. I've not decided which."

"You'll have a wide choice."

"No, I've inquired already and my selection has narrowed to two chiefs. One is Philippe Pinel, at the Salpêtrière."

"I've heard of him," interrupted Michaud. "Isn't he the man who ordered the insane to be liberated from chains and handcuffs?"

Théophile nodded. "Yes, and that appeals to me. His treatment of the demented speaks in his behalf. The other is Jean Corvisart des Marets at the Hôpital de la Charité."

Michaud lifted one finger. "Wait, the name is familiar. I think he is in great favor with the First Consul. If you join his staff he might help you swell the ranks of the successful physicians in Paris."

"Paris is not my idea. I'd much rather settle in Quimper or Brest. For the present I must choose a chief and choose him well. Tomorrow I'll go and hear Pinel, and the day after I'll go to the Charité."

The Salpêtrière reminded Théophile of the Hôtel-Dieu: it was composed of buildings separated by courtyards. He was told Pinel was lecturing in the third building on the left.

The first yard was empty. Théophile missed the hens that foraged endlessly at Nantes.

In the second yard there were about twenty women. Some were talking to themselves, some were looking ahead vacantly. One repeated again and again the same gesture of brushing off an imaginary object from her shoulder. Another was sitting on the ground, her head bent low, her long hair hiding her face. An older woman asked Théophile to take her to her son. A feeling of pity overcame him. "So, these are the insane Pinel has freed from chains. How right he was, and how sad to see them living in a world of their own."

Once in the third building, he was directed to an amphitheater and sat on the upper bench. Pinel was lecturing.

His pleasant voice filled the auditorium. He spoke fluently without looking at any notes. Théophile had the impression he was a man at the top and knew it. He was dressed in the latest fashion. An enormous double-pointed collar framed his clean shaven chin. A gold chain dangled on his vest. His gestures were somewhat theatrical as he paced behind the chair he was supposed to occupy. When he stopped, he put his hands on its back, rocked it, then pushed it away to punctuate the end of a phrase. This invariably brought applause from the crowded benches.

"Gentleman," he said, "if you have read my book, *Philosophical Classification of Disease,* you are already familiar with my ideas. Symptoms are the all-important facts of medicine."

"He is right," thought Théophile. "Symptoms lead to the core of the problem of diagnosis."

"That is the reason why," continued Pinel, "I have applied the great Linnaeus' method to medicine. What he did in botany, I do in medicine. Oh, I'm not the first to have thought of it. Dr. Sauvages did it before me," he added in a low tone tinged with false humility, "and I revised his writings to suit a more modern trend of thought." Here the chair went sliding and applause greeted the orator.

Pinel gestured as if trying to refrain the enthusiasm, waited a second, went to the table where lay a pitcher and a glass. He filled the glass, drank slowly, drew a handkerchief from his pocket, wiped his lips, grabbed the chair and sat down.

"Remember, disease is one and one only. It reveals itself through symptoms. These differ according to the constitution, the sex, the age of the patient, the climate of his country of origin, and even the season. Therefore it is of prime importance to have a clear picture of the classification of the symptoms. They must be divided, like plants, into orders, classes, and species. Then you prescribe accordingly."

"Words," murmured Théophile. "I wonder where he is going with his classification?"

". . . Twelve kinds of nausea . . . Five kinds of pains . . ."

Théophile was not listening any more. He examined the crowd. The fervor with which some were taking notes amused him. He leaned over his neighbor, who was writing feverishly. "At what time does Dr. Pinel make his rounds?"

The man did not look up. "Shhh," he said without interrupting his scribbling. Taking advantage of a burst of applause, Théophile repeated his question. The man seemed surprised. "Rounds? Why?"

"To examine the patients."

"He does not need to. His assistants do. They report the symptoms to him and he has such knowledge of their classification that he can prescribe without seeing the patients."

"Autopsies?"

The man did not see fit to answer. A shrug of his shoulders made Théophile understand the ineptitude of such a question.

"That's enough," concluded Théophile, and he left the amphitheater.

The following day he went to the Charité.

Corvisart had not arrived as yet. This gave Théophile time to look at the wards. Their orderly appearance pleased him. The curtains around the beds, the beds themselves, were clean. Some students were talking to patients. In an office adjoining the men's division, a group was holding a discussion. Théophile tried to listen. A few words reached him, just enough to make him understand that they were comparing the findings of an autopsy with the medical history of the deceased. He approached. Someone saw him and the door was shut at once. This both annoyed and amused him. "They think I'm a patient," he thought. "I'd better introduce myself." And when the meeting was over he went to the man who had led it. "My name is Laennec."

"Breton, I'm sure."

"My name does not lie."

"I'm Dr. Bayle, Dr. Corvisart's assistant. What can I do for you?"

Théophile explained that he had thought of joining Dr. Corvisart's staff.

"You'll find his teaching rewarding," began Dr. Bayle, "but you must be prepared to work and work hard. He insists on well-taken histories and he wants the autopsies correlated with the histories of the patients."

"I guessed that," interrupted Théophile. "I heard your discussion through the door and I was sorry when you closed it."

"I mistook you for a curious intruder."

"I knew you thought I was a patient." And the two laughed. A current of sympathy was born between them. A solid friendship was beginning.

While Dr. Bayle was questioning Théophile about his previous experience, Dr. Corvisart appeared. The students gathered around him. He barely acknowledged their respectful greetings and talked to Bayle only. Théophile slipped to the back of the group. He wanted to observe.

A new patient was presented. When the student had finished reading his notes Dr. Corvisart said coldly, "Incomplete and not well observed. Next case."

"I examined this man," said Bayle. "He complains of palpitations. I took his pulse—"

"You did?" interrupted Corvisart. "And what did it tell you? Everything including his mother's age?"

A sudden blush invaded Bayle's face. He answered as if he had not heard the sarcasm, "His pulse is irregular in rhythm and quality."

"Bayle, I've already told you that you are wasting your time with this mania of yours. You remind me of one of our colleagues who loves to classify symptoms, divides them into classes—ten, to be exact—forty orders, and arrives at the respectable number of twenty-four hundred species. I can't understand your enthusiasm for taking the pulse of each and every patient."

And Dr. Corvisart went to the next bed. In the regrouping Théophile found himself facing the chief, a vantage spot because of his small stature but not to his liking.

Corvisart's sarcastic expression became kinder as he leaned over the bed. "How do you feel?" The man explained that he had a sharp pain in his chest. Corvisart ordered him to remove his shirt. First he observed his breathing, then he applied his left hand flat on the exposed chest and, with the second finger of the other hand, tapped on the fingers of the flat hand. Up and down, right and left, he went tapping. When he had covered the whole thorax a smile of satisfaction appeared on his severe features. "This man," he announced, "has fluid at the base of the left lung which has displaced his heart."

Théophile had not missed a single motion. Corvisart noticed his interest and addressed him: "Do you know what percussion is?"

"Percussion," he answered, "from the Latin *percussio,* a blow of one body against another."

"And who invented it?"

This time Théophile could not answer. He ventured, "This is the first time I've seen this method used, sir. I presume you invented it."

"For your benefit, young man, I'm going to repeat what I've already said many times. Those who don't attend my rounds regularly will benefit from it also. The physician who first used percussion is Dr. Leopold Auenbrugger from Vienna. His father was an innkeeper at Gratz. Little Leopold had watched the cellar men strike light blows on the barrels to find the level of beer or wine. Where there was liquid there was a dull sound. The space where there was air sounded more like a drum.

"When little Leopold became a physician he thought of applying that method to the human body. He reasoned that the lungs, being full of air, might sound like the upper part of the barrels. The heart, which is a solid mass filled with a fluid, the blood, should give a dull sound like beer or wine. He was right.

"Like all innovators, he was laughed at. He published a small pamphlet in Latin on his discovery. That was in 1761. Nobody paid any attention to it. I was lucky enough to find it and began using percussion with success. I'm preparing a translation of that pamphlet. I expect to publish it with commentaries.

"Sometimes I wonder why people refuse to accept innovations. I suppose it is a normal human reaction."

Corvisart did not see the fleeting smile on Bayle's face.

That same evening Théophile, full of enthusiasm, announced to his brother that he was joining Corvisart's service.

CHAPTER 10

It was near the end of the month. There was little money left and Théophile and Michaud were discussing their budget and wondering what would be wiser: to have their shoes resoled and go hungry or have wet feet and eat. Suddenly Michaud exclaimed, "We should move to our own flat. It would be less expensive after the initial expenditure of buying furniture—secondhand of course." Théophile agreed.

A few days later Michaud announced that he had found the ideal place, a room near the Place St. Michel. "It would cost about eighty francs to get it furnished, and we could eat at Père Marin's in the Rue St. Jacques. One sou for a plate of soup, five for a portion of meat."

Théophile said it sounded like a life of luxury, and at the beginning of July they moved to their own home.

A year later success had come to the hard-working brothers. In June 1802 they were able to "lay down their laurels at their father's feet." That was the way Michaud announced he had won the first prize in French literature, in Latin, and in French grammar.

At the other end of the table Théophile, in a soberer style, was writing:

My dear Papa,

If you are interested in autopsies I'll send you the latest number of the *Journal of Medicine*, edited by Corvisart and Le Roux, where you'll find an article signed by your Théophile: "Observation on a case of heart disease." I'm preparing another article on the inflammations of the peritoneum, the membrane which lines the inner wall of the abdomen.

I'm not taking any vacation this summer. I've agreed, at my chief's insistence, to try for the entrance examination at the Ecole Pratique. It requires a great deal of preparation.

The article on the inflammations of the peritoneum was published in August 1802: "Report of six cases based on personal observation in Dr. Corvisart's service, followed by autopsies."

For the first time peritonitis was identified and differenciated from enteritis, gastritis, and hepatitis, specific diseases of the intestines, stomach, and liver respectively.

For the first time the characteristic appearance of a patient suffering from peritonitis was described accurately: "The facial features seem contracted and pulled toward the forehead."

For the first time the appellation of milk fever was refuted. It was the name given to the then prevalent fever that killed many new mothers because a white liquid, presumed to be milk, was found in their abdomens. Without the help of a microscope, Théophile affirmed that it was not milk but the result of peritoneal inflammation and that peritonitis was the cause of their death.

That article revolutionized hitherto widely accepted opinions and brought its young author a great deal of attention.

In September of the same year Théophile entered the Ecole Pratique after passing the entrance examination. He was going to work under Bayle, who was the lecturer in anatomy. That pleased him; and the professors, Bichat and Dupuytren, fulfilled his ideal. Both were interested in research.

Bichat was preparing a work on pathological anatomy to complete a textbook of anatomy which he had already published. He was not to teach Théophile for long, nor would he ever finish his second treatise. He died in July 1803 at the age of thirty-one.

Dupuytren, six years older than Théophile, was a hard master, domineering and vindictive. He had had a difficult beginning, fighting hunger and poverty. This had left him bitter, greedy for gain, and jealous. Through indomitable will power and arduous work he had attained his present position and he was conscious of his worth. He was admired, feared, and universally detested.

He became interested in Théophile's exceptional mind and did not consider him a competitor since it was clear the young Breton wanted to practice in his native province. Thus assured, Dupuytren asked Théophile to collaborate on his own *Pathological Anatomy*. However, master and pupil disagreed on the meaning of "collaboration." Dupuytren had no intention of letting it be known that he relied on an assistant. He wanted to publish under his name alone all the research done under him.

Théophile rebelled. Words were exchanged and the collaboration ended abruptly when Dupuytren, after Bichat's death, used part of the unfinished Bichat's *Pathological Anatomy* as his own.

In the meantime, Théophile continued to write with Corvisart's support. In January 1803 he published an article on the functions of the bursa of the shoulder. In February he revised some of Glisson's works. Glisson, in 1642, had described the membrane enveloping the liver as a fold of the peritoneum. Théophile refuted that opinion. "It is a real membrane of a different texture."

When Bayle congratulated him on his discovery, Théophile said he would use it as the subject of his doctoral thesis. Encouraged by Corvisart, he planned to write it in what he called his spare time—nights. It took two nights to write fifty-two pages. When it was finished, he collapsed.

Revising it, he was not satisfied and refused to use it for his thesis. He published it and it was received favorably.

In the midst of rising fame, jealousies, and hard work, Théophile had to face financial difficulties. A new roommate, Jacques Varanne, from Nantes, had joined the brothers, and the three moved to larger and more expensive quarters above Père Marin's restaurant. Now Michaud was leaving. He had been offered a position at Beauvais by the prefect. Papa Laennec, taking advantage of this, had discontinued the allowance.

With no money in prospect, the rent presented a problem. Generously Jacques assumed more than his share. This left the question of food. Théophile went looking for a paid occupation. He was asked to ghost-write for a would-be scientific author. He would not think of it, but he consented to correct some medical papers, a tedious and poorly compensated task. Le Roux guessed his plight and offered to help him. Proudly, Théophile refused. That same day, driven by necessity, he sold his gold watch to pay arrears on food bills.

At the beginning of the summer a new competition was announced for August. It was open to all medical students from the three Schools of Medicine: Paris, Montpellier, and Strasbourg. The subjects to be covered were surgery, med-

icine, anatomy, and chemistry. It meant work and Théophile spent many nights over his books. He would not
take time to go to bed, and to Jacques's friendly scolding
he invariably answered, "I can't sleep in this hot room. It's
my old asthma. I'm more comfortable sitting up. I might
just as well take advantage of it."

The big day arrived. First test on the cadaver: amputa-
tion of the humerus at the shoulder. Dupuytren was the
assistant and Dr. Dubois the examiner. "Elegant technique," was his comment after Théophile had finished.
Then followed the written examinations: three hours for
each subject.

After a week of anxiety, the candidates met to hear the
results. The amphitheater was thronged and noisy. As Théophile and Bayle pushed through the crowded benches a
secretary entered. There was a sudden hush. He read in a
monotonous voice: "First prize, Laennec, from Dr. Corvisart's staff."

"Ohs" and "Ahs" and applause burst out but were
quickly hushed. Unimpressed, the secretary continued:
"Medicine, two first prizes, Laennec, already named, and
Billerey from Dr. Pinel's staff." More applause, and the
rest of the list was drowned in the tumult.

"I should have been named second," Théophile whispered. "They always use alphabetical order."

The secretary tried to be heard above the noise. "The

official distribution of the awards will take place on the third of September, in the Hall of the Caryatids at the Louvre. The recipients of the first prizes will receive an invitation from His Excellency, Monsieur Chaptal, Minister of Education, to attend a banquet the same evening."

This announcement left Théophile in a quandary. His wardrobe was inappropriate. Bonaparte, now Consul for life, and Madame Bonaparte had revived the elegance of the past century and made formal attire compulsory at official functions. Impossible to buy a new suit. No money. Théophile tried to borrow one but his friends were taller and better nourished than he. Père Marin's menus were not conducive to plumpness. Finally he rented a suit.

At the Louvre he was the center of attention. At the banquet Chaptal congratulated him. "I understand," he said, "that you were eligible for other prizes but the others had to be encouraged."

Later it became known that he had been nominated for the prize in medicine, but Pinel had insisted that his pupil, Billerey, share it. His only concession was to let Laennec be named first.

Shortly afterward the annual examination of the Ecole Pratique was posted. It was not compulsory but Théophile sent in his application. To his surprise, he was summoned to the director's office and asked to withdraw his application. It seemed that only one other student had been willing to take the examination. "They are afraid to compete with you," said the director.

Théophile bowed. *"Monsieur le directeur,* your wish is law. I will desist if you so desire. Still I don't feel I'm guilty of being a scarecrow."

It was Théophile's dream to teach. Corvisart planned to have him give a series of lectures at the Ecole Pratique. He had not counted on Dupuytren's jealous nature. As soon as the project became known, the irascible professor went to see Théophile and told him *he* was going to lecture. Teaching was not a student's prerogative. The interview was stormy and Théophile could do nothing but give up his dream.

Corvisart was greatly disappointed. Immediately he organized a series of private lectures to be given by Théophile. He liked his brilliant student and was glad to show his appreciation. He was glad also to do it to spite the widely detested Dupuytren.

Curiosity and genuine interest spurred the registration and it was before a full auditorium that Théophile gave his first lecture in November 1803.

An atmosphere of expectation pervaded the amphitheater as the new lecturer was awaited.

A small, pale, thin man entered. Those who did not know him were surprised at his youthful appearance. His fame had made them forget he was only twenty-one.

A sudden flush colored his cheeks as prolonged applause greeted him. He walked briskly to the chair, sat down, disposed a few notes on the table, and pulled his cuffs nervously. He waited until silence was established, then addressed the class. At first his phrases were short, choppy, his voice muffled, but he never hesitated. Words came out easily.

His plan was for three lectures a week, fifty in all. First he would cover anatomy, then the diseases of each anatomic system, and last, the pathology of the different organs as observed in autopsies.

Little by little he gained assurance, the phrases became well rounded, his voice increased in strength. He paid homage to Bichat, calling him a pioneer in that new science, pathology. Forgetting his grudge against Dupuytren, he acknowledged his pre-eminence as an investigator and teacher and did not overlook Bayle, who had directed his first steps in the field of research.

Toward the end of the lecture, he had overcome the stage fright inherent in a beginner and revealed himself a clear and concise orator in complete mastery of the expression of his thoughts.

⤳ CHAPTER 11

Seven o'clock in the morning. Complete darkness outside. The inconspicuous figure of a small man was going down the stairway to the basement of the Charité. He opened the door of the autopsy room. No light. He stumbled against a table. "Jérôme!" he called.

Dragging steps echoed in the hall and an old man appeared carrying a candle. "Good morning, Monsieur Laennec. Everything is ready."

"Good morning, Jérôme. I'm sorry I made you come down at this early hour but I want to do this autopsy before my lecture at ten."

Jérôme, the orderly, lit a kerosene lamp on the wall and put his candle on the table where the instruments shone. He removed the sheet from the stone slab in the center of the room. A cadaver lay on it.

Théophile took off his coat, rolled up his sleeves, and wrapped an apron around his waist. He chose a knife and

made the first incision. For more than an hour he worked
silently, examining the organs one by one. He made constant use of a magnifying glass and lifted fragments of
tissue near the lamp to see better.

Jérôme was sitting against the wall, smoking his pipe.
From time to time he got up and changed the water in the
basin where Théophile cleansed his hands.

A gray dawn filtered through the windows. Théophile
noticed it. "I certainly could use more light," he said.

For an answer, Jérôme puffed more vigorously on his
pipe.

The door was pushed open. "May I come in?"

"Pierre Bayle! Please, do come in."

"What are you doing?"

"A case of collapse of the vertebrae. You remember
Bed Number 3? And those cold abscesses that kept draining from his back?" Théophile's voice warmed up as he
spoke. "Everything is healthy but his lungs. Now, the
spine. Jérôme!"

Jérôme approached, his pipe between his teeth. He lifted
the corpse and placed it back up. The opening of an abscess
could be seen above the waist. Théophile probed it. "I can
touch the bone," he said. He made an incision and exposed
the diseased spine. Bayle seized the magnifying glass and
bent over. "You were right, tubercles."

"I expected them. Tubercles in his lungs, in his spine.

Here they are soft, hence the collapse of the vertebrae. In other cases, I have found tubercles in the liver, the kidneys, the larynx. Some like grains of millet, some as large as lentils, some hard, some soft. Pierre, I can affirm that where I found tubercles the patients were afflicted with the same disease, regardless of the organs invaded."

"How do you explain the ten or twelve kinds of phthisis some authors have described?"

"Nonsense. Phthisis is one. I have examined the lungs of many cases diagnosed as phthisis. Only a few showed tubercles. The rest should not have been labeled phthisis."

While speaking, Théophile removed the diseased vertebra, held it on the table, and reached for a saw. At the first thrust it slipped and fresh blood, Théophile's blood, spurted on the table. He dropped everything and plunged his hand in the basin. Bayle looked at the wound. The saw had penetrated deeply into the flesh of the left index finger and it was bleeding freely.

"Jérôme," said Bayle, "fetch a dressing from the ward."

Théophile sat down, holding his finger with a handkerchief. "Now I'm handicapped for a few days. At least I finished this autopsy. I needed this last bit of information for my lecture at ten."

Jérôme and his pipe had returned. He handed a chunk of lint and a bandage to Bayle, who dressed the wound while he talked. "I have a piece of news for you. These tubercles almost made me forget it. Do you know that Dupuytren sends spies to your lectures?"

"I don't doubt it."

"When he speaks of you it is to criticize your ideas. After you made the distinction between the 'encephaloid,' the soft tumor, and the 'scirrhus,' the hard type, he insisted he had found it before you."

"He probably did. He had done enough autopsies not to have missed them but I coined the words. Encephaloid because it has the consistency of the brain and scirrhus from the Greek *skirros,* hard."

"Now this is the news. Dupuytren is launching a new society, the Society of Anatomy. I think you should belong to it, whether he likes it or not."

"I'll join it," said Théophile. "It will be amusing to watch his reaction. I'll probably be asked to speak and I have a paper ready on cardiac anomalies in newborn babies. My article on human parasites is not finished. I found three cases of cysts in the liver and I'm looking for a fourth one. Those cysts are of a parasitic nature and are not due to a degeneration of the liver tissue. I looked at them under a microscope. That gave me the clue to the problem. You should get a microscope, Pierre, it is a great help."

Bayle laughed. "Wait until Dupuytren hears that you use a microscope. He'll explode!"

"What a pity such a great man is afflicted with such a

temper," deplored Théophile, and in a different tone asked, "What time is it? I've . . . forgotten my watch."

Bayle knew the watch had been forgotten constantly in recent weeks. "What a pity," he thought, "that such a great man had to sell his watch in order to live." He glanced at his watch. "Almost ten."

"Time to go."

At the stroke of ten Théophile, his left hand bandaged, entered the amphitheater.

ᄆᄆ CHAPTER 12

R esearch and teaching did not divert Théophile from completing his studies. His next and last step was to write a thesis for his doctorate. In May 1804 he submitted "Propositions on Hippocrates' doctrine in relation to the practice of medicine." It was dedicated to Dr. Guillaume Laennec, which aroused his father's jealousy. On the eleventh of June he was convoked to discuss it before a board of five examiners.

On that day the great hall of the School of Medicine was thronged. Friends, students, even enemies had come to hear what promised to be an interesting event. Théophile was known for his outspoken and fearless manners. What would he say before the conservative elements of the board? And what would they say?

The five professors entered majestically, arrayed in the scarlet robes of their office, ermine paws on one shoulder, their heads topped with a high fluted cap of the same color.

Corvisart, the president, led them. A fugitive smile flashed on his stern face when he saw Théophile. Following Corvisart came Baudeloque, Chaussier, Boyer, and Deyeux. They sat on one side of a long table covered with green felt, opened the copies of the thesis, and a secretary called, "René Théophile Hyacinthe Laennec," in a bleating voice.

Théophile whispered to Bayle, who had accompanied him, "I had almost forgotten my third name."

"Good luck," answered Bayle.

"The candidate will please be seated," bleated the secretary.

Théophile took his place on the other side of the table and Corvisart began. "I have read with great interest, as my distinguished colleagues have, I am sure, your 'Propositions on Hippocrates' doctrine.' Before discussing it, I'll give a rapid sketch of its content."

"This is for those who have not read it," thought Théophile. "They seldom do anyway."

"In a preface you show the danger of systematizing and you praise Hippocrates for having been free from it.

"In the first part you explain the method of the Father of Medicine.

"In the second you tell of the relation of his doctrine to the practice of medicine.

"Tertio, you give your personal comments on Hippocrates' method and doctrine and your opinion on the observation of symptoms as the sole guide to diagnosis and prognosis.

"I will now ask my colleagues to take over. Dr. Boyer?"

Boyer, who had dozed during the lengthy introduction, came to life and asked, "What is Hippocrates' method?"

"His method is based on observation alone," Théophile replied in a clear voice. "In fact, he cautions his followers not to accept a principle until confirmed by repeated experiments. This is widely accepted today."

"And what do you call his doctrine? To me it is the same."

Used to speaking in public, Théophile was not embarrassed. "It cannot be abridged in a few words, sir. His method is his way of proceeding, his doctrine what he thinks to be the truth. Hippocrates describes two kinds of symptoms. Some, such as fever, delirium, insomnia, are universal and are common to many diseases. Others are peculiar to one certain disease. These last lead to diagnosis, although Hippocrates was not interested in that phase of medicine. The first mentioned, the universal symptoms, weighed through experience, permit a prognosis which, in Hippocrates' time, was the most important problem. We have accepted his method but we are free to reject his doctrine, since diagnosis is now the main object of medicine."

Corvisart nodded approvingly. Boyer mumbled, "I thank

you," and Théophile thought, "I hope you understood. Now you can go back to sleep."

It was Baudeloque's turn. He adjusted his glasses and thumbed the copy of the thesis. "Monsieur Laennec, I was impressed by your opinion on the nature of fever. As head of the Maternité, I have a wide experience in that matter. Kindly develop your ideas."

"This one is not asleep," thought Théophile. He answered, "Fever is a symptom, sir, not a disease. The disease should be treated, then the fever will disappear."

Deyeux interrupted him. "Don't universal symptoms show that disease is one and one only but presents itself under different aspects according to the individual?"

"No," exclaimed Théophile with vivacity. "I'm not of the opinion of those who say: one malady, one remedy. Disease is not one. There are many diseases. We know it now. Autopsies, unthought of in Hippocrates' time, have opened the door to pathology, hence the accurate art of diagnosis. I think the patient should be examined and the disease diagnosed before attempting any treatment."

Deyeux lifted his eyebrows. He was an ardent follower of Pinel and felt this was a direct attack on his master.

Chaussier, who had not spoken yet, raised his hand. "May I ask the candidate if he intends to discard the treatments in favor for centuries?"

"I'll retain those which have given proof of their efficacy. This is in accord with Hippocrates' method."

"Rather revolutionary," Deyeux whispered to Chaussier. Chaussier, his hand near his ear, made him repeat the remark. Baudeloque heard it. He frowned and raised his voice. "Since we all agree to accept Hippocrates' method, based on proven facts, we could do it for treatment as well as diagnosis." This was obviously for the benefit of his colleagues.

Corvisart felt the discussion was veering toward the personal school of thought of the other members of the board and he did not want it to become acrimonious. He got up as if declaring the end of the examination.

"Which translation did you use?" asked Baudeloque, still seated.

Partly annoyed and partly amused by the debate, Théophile answered with animation, "I never relied on translation. As the Italians say: *traduttore, traditore* [translator, traitor]. I read Greek."

Whispers of admiration rose from the audience. Corvisart let his gavel down to obtain silence and declared the candidate had fulfilled the required conditions to receive his diploma of Doctor of Medicine. Applause burst. Théophile bowed. The five professors left as majestically as they had come and Théophile joined Bayle. Well-wishers were clos-

ing in on him. He dismissed them with an impatient gesture and went away with his friend.

Moments later they were sitting in the Luxembourg
Gardens, near the Fontaine Médicis, Théophile's favorite
place. He liked the seclusion of that dark alley shaded by
the dense foliage, the dormant waters of the pool, the dif-
fused light that played on the stone figures of Polyphemus
threatening Acis and Galatea frozen in their violent passions.

Théophile breathed deeply. For the first time in many
days his asthma did not trouble him. He closed his eyes.
Bayle respected his silence. A ball rolled at their feet. Romping children rushed to retrieve it. Before they could, Théophile had awakened from his dream. He picked it up and
threw it back at them. "I should not be lazy," he said.

"You, lazy? That's news. I bet you were hatching plans
for future research."

A bitter smile contracted Théophile's mouth. "I must
make money. I have to live and I'm indebted to my uncle.
Without him I could not have paid the 880 francs needed to
print my thesis. My father does not like to loosen his purse
strings. I have changed my plans. I'm going to open an
office here. I've rented a small apartment a door from yours,
5 Rue du Jardinet. I'll move in the fall. Jacques Varanne
is leaving for Nantes and my cousin Christophe is coming
to study law."

"Practice may be slow in the beginning. How will you pay the rent?"

"I've had an offer to collaborate on a medical dictionary. That will pay the rent, which is modest. The landlady has been very reasonable in her demand. She is from Brittany."

"Really? What a coincidence," laughed Bayle.

"We Bretons are rather clannish as you may know."

"And the food bills? You'll have to eat occasionally."

"I hope my patients will pay for them. Also I'll have another source of income. Through Corvisart I'm going to be a member of the Society of the School of Medicine and I'm promised a small remuneration for a column in their *Journal:* reports on new books and articles."

"For relaxation?"

"Chamber music with a congenial group."

"Bretons?"

"Most of them."

Dusk surprised them and they parted. Théophile walked home alone.

CHAPTER 13

In July 1804, as expected, Théophile became a member of the Society of the School of Medicine and wrote for its *Journal*. It was not long before he was the target of attacks and in November the fight was on. Dupuytren criticized Dr. Laennec in an article.

Théophile answered in the *Journal* of the Society and and did not hesitate to proclaim Bichat responsible for the start of the new science, pathology.

Dupuytren "exploded" as Bayle had predicted and in violent terms accused Dr. Laennec of ungratefulness and plagiarism.

Théophile, in a dignified article, reminded the irascible professor, whose science and talent he respected, "of facts that might not please him if known." Had the fight continued, he was ready to divulge Dupuytren's unscrupulous custom of publishing as his own the work and research done by the others.

At this point the *Journal of Medicine* refused to have any further part in the polemic and it ended there.

However, Dupuytren's methods had been revealed and Bichat given the place he deserved. Bayle refused to collaborate with Dupuytren and joined Théophile, who was planning to write his own pathological anatomy. It was to be called "Visible alterations of the human body in the state of disease." Through the years Théophile was to accumulate eight hundred pages of information. It was never published.

The end of 1804 was a period of rejoicing all over France. Napoleon was crowned Emperor by Pope Pius VII. Théophile, among other officials, was granted an audience on December 26.

The year 1805 saw the opening of Dr. R. T. Laennec's office, empty most of the time, and the continuation of his work. The rent was paid regularly. In September, Théophile, incapacitated by attacks of asthma, headaches, and insomnia, thought of taking a vacation. He chose to visit his cousin, Annick de Pompery, at Couvrelles, between Soissons and Rheims, and arrived on a bright crisp day. The Château de Couvrelles was an imposing mansion flanked by stables and a glass-enclosed orangery. A moat separated it from a farm and the wooded estate extended for miles around.

Théophile was shown into the living room. The louvers were shut and in the dim light he saw a woman sewing near the window. Mistaking her for his cousin, he exclaimed, "Here I am!" and stopped short. It was not Madame de Pompery.

The woman had jumped to her feet, her scissors fell on the floor, and a cry of surprise escaped from her lips. They looked at each other, embarrassed. Théophile approached, picked up the scissors. "I'm sorry," he said, "if I've frightened you. I'm Théophile Laennec."

The woman whispered, *"Merci, monsieur.* I am Madame Argou, Madame de Pompery's godchild," and trying to hide her confusion, she opened the louvers. In the bright light Théophile could see her young and sensitive features. She was not pretty but there was a serene harmony in her soft brown eyes and her calm face framed by wavy dark hair. Obviously in mourning, her black dress was simple and she wore no jewelry. Before Théophile could engage in a conversation, she had disappeared and Annick de Pompery was in the room.

"Cousin Théophile, bonjour!"

Théophile bowed and raised her hand to his lips. She laughed. "No court manners between us. Just a big old-fashioned hug and kiss." And the two sat down, happy to evoke memories and to exchange news. That relayed by Théophile was distressing. Michaud had suffered a pulmonary hemorrhage and Uncle Michel had died of phthisis of the lungs in Southampton. "I felt it was time I took a rest," said Théophile, trying to sound cheerful, "before it is too late. Health is a fleeting treasure. We begin to appreciate it the day it leaves us. I've not begun yet."

Madame de Pompery was not deceived by the tone of the remark. She felt an undercurrent of sadness in his irony. She had guessed her cousin was in poor health. His pallor, his emaciated features spelled exhaustion. She did not want to show her concern and shifted the topic. "My husband, my son, my daughter, my guests—everybody went hiking. I'm alone with Jaquette."

"You mean Madame Argou? I frightened her when I made a most informal entrance."

"Jaquette is shy. By the way, you may know her family. She was born Jaquette Guichard, twenty-four years ago."

"In Brest, I'm sure."

"In Brest. What a memory! When she was left destitute after her husband's death I asked her to come and live with us. She rarely smiles. I count on you to make her laugh."

"I'll try."

Théophile's stay at Couvrelles proved to be an ideal vacation. Long walks improved his asthma. Headaches disappeared and he slept soundly. His old energy back, he went hunting, he went canoeing. He played chess with Monsieur de Pompery and won invariably. He organized concerts and wrote comedies. He played the flute, he danced, and not only did he succeed in making Jaquette laugh but she took a part in a charade to everybody's amazement. Under her guidance and Cousin Annick's he perfected his knowledge of Breton.

At the end of September he went back to Paris and Jaquette laughed no more.

Upon his arrival he had the pleasant surprise of being named chief editor of the *Journal,* with an increase in salary, and more patients filled his office. Some had not hesitated to travel from the remote provinces to consult him.

Théophile had nurtured great plans for 1807. He had been tempted to have his own carriage, but after a survey of his budget he abandoned the idea as too expensive and felt that a larger office was a more urgent need. He found what he wanted next door. Bayle was getting married and had to change his residence. In January, Théophile leased his friend's former apartment, hired a cook, Angélique, and moved from Number 5 to Number 3 Rue du Jardinet.

That same year three professorships became vacant at the Paris Hôtel-Dieu. Théophile had hopes. When the list of new appointments was published his name did not appear. No one, except Bayle perhaps, ever knew the depth of his disappointment, which he hid under a feigned indifference.

In March 1807 the professor of external pathology, Dr. Lassus, died. It was rumored that Dupuytren, then director of anatomical research, would get it and that Théophile would replace Dupuytren. Three months later Richerand replaced Lassus, Dupuytren kept his position, and once more Théophile was passed by.

He found consolation in other activities. On April 16 he read a report on an unusual kind of hernia before the Society of the School, and, apropos of an essay on medicine of the Arabs by Dr. Amoreux, he wrote a well-informed article demonstrating that the Arabs had followed the Syrians and the Persians, who were heirs to the Greco-Roman physicians.

In the *Journal,* for which he wrote regularly, he mentioned a charming bit of poetry by J. L. F. Terr called *Hygeia, or the Art of Being Well and Staying Well.* He commented on it humorously and added a complete list of all the poems written about medicine from antiquity to the present.

His constant search for the truth led him to explode Gall's doctrine. Dr. Gall was the exponent of a new science, phrenology, the study of the protuberances of the skull. Each, according to him, corresponded to an increase of development in the part of the brain directly under it. Hence the palpation of the twenty-six humps of a head permitted a complete analysis of the subject's character and the evaluation of his talents.

Théophile's article, or rather articles (there were three), disproved the so-called scientific aspect of Gall's doctrine through logic and common sense.

Next he attacked and refuted John Brown's system. From Edinburgh, the Scot's ideas had swept over England and the Continent. According to him, the state of disease was due to an imbalance of stimulation in the body. Too much of it brought certain diseases; not enough allowed the development of others. When Brown classified phthisis among those caused by an accumulation of stimuli and denied the existence of tubercles, Théophile advised him to investigate more thoroughly. He wrote in the *Journal:* "I have autopsied hundreds of phthisics and I have still to find one who did not show tubercles."

At the beginning of 1808, Théophile could look back upon his accomplishments and be satisfied. The income from his practice, which had brought him four hundred francs in 1805, had grown to twenty-four hundred. Perhaps he could soon afford a vacation in Brittany, perhaps he would get a hospital position, perhaps, at last, he would have peace of mind.

He had not counted on his family.

CHAPTER 14

Bayle, in answer to an urgent message from Angélique, had rushed to Théophile's bedside. His fears were well warranted. Théophile was sitting near the open window, propped up by cushions. Dark circles made his eyes seem more deeply set, his breathing was labored. He smiled at his friend. Instinctively Bayle put his fingers on Théophile's wrist. "Rapid but regular and of good quality. You need a rest. Why don't you go to your father's for a while?"

Théophile made an effort to speak but was stopped by a fit of coughing. Bayle looked at him intently as he wiped his lips. Théophile had followed his eyes. "No," he said, "no blood . . . yet." He got up, refused to be helped, and staggered to his desk. He removed a drawer and from a secret place took out some letters. "These will tell you why I will not go to my father's. Read."

Bayle went over the pages rapidly. "Your father is having a jolly time."

"Yes, open house every evening and high gambling stakes. Result: debts and more debts. Served with court papers, my father sold two pieces of property and mortgaged others. On the eve of being involved in a scandal, he invited my brother to take a vacation in Brittany."

Théophile gasped. After a while he continued, "I received a letter from Michaud yesterday. Michaud, not knowing the motive behind the offer, went to Quimper. He had to fight debtors and clear up a mass of judicial papers. Some were missing. They were at St. Brieuc. Sick as he was, recuperating from a pulmonary hemorrhage, he traveled through rain and fog to St. Brieuc. Once there, he discovered that our father had spent all of our mother's estate and taken the money that should have gone to my uncle Guillaume. The worst was yet to come. An imperial decree discharged him in the wake of reports of irregularities in his administration. And, having lost his position, my father is coming here, as my uninvited guest, to plead his cause before the Emperor. Nobody knows of what my father is capable. He is a genius when it comes to attracting attention."

A week later Papa Laennec arrived at the Rue du Jardinet. Angélique was watching from behind the curtains. She saw a sprightly gentleman alight from a luxurious carriage, dressed in the fashion of the past century: knee

breeches, a dark blue cape, and a tricorne. The driver lined
up five pieces of luggage on the sidewalk. "How long is
he going to stay?" she lamented. As the knocker fell re-
peatedly, she mumbled, "I'll keep you waiting. You'll be
in soon enough."

"Angélique, I presume. *Bonjour,* Angélique, my son's
aegis."

"His what? . . . I don't speak Breton, monsieur."

"Aegis means kind protector. It is a name taken from
Greek mythology. It is a compliment."

"I don't speak Greek, monsieur."

"You don't need to. Now, Angélique, please, fetch my
glorious son."

"The doctor is making calls. He'll be back later."

"Don't tell me his patients come before the man who
begot him and placed him on the pinnacle of success."

Angélique did not answer. "I wish he'd speak French
and not patois," she grumbled as she showed him in.

Papa Laennec inspected the place. "Cheap furniture, not
impressive enough for a prominent physician." He pushed
a door. "His office? Hmm! Bare. He should have more
chairs and tables." He thumbed some papers. "Ah, the list
of his patients. Countess . . . Baron . . . General . . .
and a minister of the government. If I don't get reinstated
with Théophile hobnobbing with influential people, I'll be
surprised."

When Théophile came home he found a number of

patients in his waiting room and, arrayed in an elegant brocade coat, his father playing cards with one of them. Their meeting was affectionate and theatrical. Papa Laennec could not have dreamed of a better setting: a crowd of on-lookers as father and son embraced after a long separation.

I his was only the beginning. Papa Laennec had an un-failing talent for commanding attention. He wrote to prominent personalities, sent a poem to the Emperor, and never hesitated to appear in the parlor when he felt sure that high officials were waiting.

Théophile, divided between respect for his father and irritation at his inconsiderate behavior, was taken ill. In the spring, harassed, he declared he was going to Couvrelles. Papa Laennec understood and planned his departure.

The day he left came the news of his reinstatement to his old position at Quimper. A victorious Roman Emperor could not have made a more triumphant return home.

The year 1808 did not bring an end to the problems that Michaud was trying to solve and 1809 saw them culmi-nate in a thunderous climax.

Michaud demanded an accounting of their mother's estate. Papa Laennec refused and, in face of mounting ex-penses, attempted to sell a piece of property. He was stopped by a court order from his three children. Furious, he sued Michaud for violation of domicile and theft of legal papers.

After such an upheaval it was difficult for the family to live under the same roof. Marie-Anne left for Kerlouarnec, a country house that was to go to Théophile, Michaud stayed in the Rue du Quay, and the Laennecs, Monsieur and Madame, moved to another part of the town.

On August 29, 1809, the little city of Quimper was given food for gossip in many months to come. Father and son testified against each other. Both knew the law. Both were eloquent: Papa Laennec, witty, brilliant, happy to be the center of attention; Michaud, pale, ailing, sure of his rights and merciless to the man who had robbed his children of their due.

On August 29 the verdict was pronounced. Papa Laennec was ordered to compensate Uncle Guillaume and to repay their mother's bequest to her three children. On them rested the responsibility of assuming the debts he had contracted before his second marriage. The settlement of the first Madame Laennec's estate took all he had.

His second wife, humiliated, left him and Théophile, heartbroken at the outcome of the trial, sent a large sum of money to his father, unaware that the irrepressible Papa intended to sue him on some fanciful pretense.

Michaud never recuperated from the strain. Alone in the ancestral house, he declined rapidly. As the end approached his father visited him, and Michaud, a victim of pulmonary tuberculosis, died on January 10, 1810.

☒ CHAPTER 15

Twice Théophile had refused to answer Angé-lique's call for dinner. He was finishing an arti-cle. After he had penned the title: *"De angina pectoris commentarius,"* he hit the table with his fist. "It is not a spasm. Jenner was right. Angina pec-toris is caused by a lesion of the coronary vessels of the heart."

The sound of voices interrupted his reflections and, for-getting to knock first, Angélique rushed in. "Mademoiselle is here!"

Used to her outbursts, Théophile said calmly, "Made-moiselle who?"

"Mademoiselle, Mademoiselle Marie-Anne!"

"My sister?"

A small figure in mourning threw herself into his open arms. Between sobs, she said she had had enough of Brit-tany and thought it was her duty to take care of the only brother she had now. "I'll be your little *maman*. Don't chase me," she added coyly.

How could he? So Marie-Anne joined Théophile's household in April 1810.

In the beginning things worked out smoothly but soon Marie-Anne showed what she was—a true Laennec like her father, spendthrift, irresponsible, and erratic, with no conception of time or money.

One afternoon, coming from a walk in the rain, she stuffed her shoes with paper "to keep them in shape," while Théophile was hunting for the missing pages of the *Journal of Medicine*.

At other times she forgot important engagements or mixed up the dates, and, worst of all, she antagonized Angélique. Théophile, tired at the end of a strenuous day, had to restore peace between his methodical maid and his unstable sister. According to her frame of mind, she loved Paris or hated it and was ready to go back to Nantes to see her new cousin, Emmanuel, the last of Aunt Désirée's sons.

Théophile would listen and say nothing.

Summer came. Good tidings lifted everybody's mood. An impressive letter bearing the imperial seal advised Dr. René Théophile Laennec that, upon the recommendation of Monsignor de Quélen, he was appointed personal physician to Joseph Cardinal Fesch, the Emperor's uncle.

Angélique, proud of her master's achievement, announced the news to all the shopkeepers in the neighborhood and Marie-Anne exulted. When told there was a compensation of three thousand francs yearly, she devised ways of spending it. Théophile refused to listen to her suggestions.

"Maybe I could be presented at court?"

"Marie-Anne, please. This is not a court assignment."

And Marie-Anne cried at the thought that she would not meet the Emperor.

If 1810 had awakened hopes of teaching in Théophile's mind, 1811 saw them shattered once more.

The chair of "Hippocrates' doctrine and rare cases," which had been held by Thouret, became vacant at his death. A good Hellenist was needed and, besides Théophile, there was only one other possible candidate, Dr. Mercy.

Months passed, appointments were announced, and the post remained empty.

In April 1811 the chair was suppressed and Théophile wrote of his disappointment to his father:

What I regret most is the added income that would have brought me security and the assurance that I could take care of you in the years to come. Now my dream is to retire in Brittany and practice medicine among the humble people. In my spare time I would edit the extensive material accumulated in my younger years, a prospect more rewarding than that of teaching in an official capacity.

In the meantime, Théophile continued to attend an ever increasing clientele. In his waiting room the poor, assured of free care, sat next to such prominent people as Chateaubriand, Madame de Staël, or the Spanish ambassador, and, of course, all the Breton colony.

In his private life, no peace. Marie-Anne behaved like a thoughtless child and was jealous of his professional activities. Things came to a climax when Théophile insisted on spending night after night at the bedside of a dying woman. In a fit of temper Marie-Anne reproached him with neglect and once more declared that she hated Paris and was going back to Brittany, this time to Quimper.

"Very well," said Théophile, "you may go but before you leave I must give you an account of the state of our finances. Sit down and listen to me. I have finished wiping away the debts our father contracted prior to his second marriage. If you remember, this was a court order. It has taken most of our inheritance. I had to sell our homestead at Quimper."

Marie-Anne, who had listened dreamily, woke up at these words. "Why did you do that? I loved our old house."

"So did I, but I had to. However, Kerlouarnec is still ours."

"You should have sold Kerlouarnec. I hate it."

"I have hopes of retiring there someday. That's the reason why I kept it. If you don't want part of it I'll give you an annuity of a hundred francs a month in exchange."

Marie-Anne ventured, "I'd prefer a lump sum."

Théophile was adamant. "It would not take long for our father to get hold of your money and you would be destitute. If you spend your allowance foolishly, at least it will come again each month."

She agreed to it and in August 1812 left for Quimper.

Once alone, Théophile wrote his will. His cousins were named heirs with the obligation to keep up the annuity to his sister should she outlive him. To Ambroise and Mériadec, who were both studying medicine, he bequeathed all his manuscripts, books, and papers.

In September he received a letter from Christophe announcing his forthcoming marriage and encouraging the whole world and his cousin to do likewise.

Théophile answered, "Celibacy has its advantages. I cannot imagine myself bound to any woman I know, less to one I don't know."

⤳ CHAPTER 16

Spring in Paris. The candle-shaped flowers of the chestnut trees had already appeared among the large leaves. Spots of green showed along the streets and parks. The air was light, the city was quiet—too quiet—on that evening of March 31, 1814. The Parisians, at the news of the defeat of Napoleon's armies, had fled before the invasion. The Empress and her son had left the Tuileries and there had been rumors of the Emperor's abdication.

Théophile and Bayle were walking in the Champs-Elysées. Before them the unfinished Arc de Triomphe was bathed in the glory of the sunset. In the distance the thud of axes could be heard felling the trees to feed the bivouac fires. Around them the small horses of the steppes were grazing on the new grass, and farther away a group of soldiers were singing and dancing. The Tsar's armies were camping in Paris.

A woman passed by. "We should have run away, all of us," she said, sobbing.

"A flight is humiliating and useless," murmured Théophile. "I sent my manuscripts and my portrait painted by Dubois to my cousins but I would never have consented to leave."

"If you had gone, what would have happened to the Breton soldiers?"

Théophile smiled at the thought of his "children." "Poor chaps who can't speak French. I never was so happy as when I was given complete charge of them in a special ward at the Salpêtrière." And he continued to muse. "Happy those who have been spared these tragic hours. Michaud . . . Aunt Désirée . . . Seven months since I received news of her death. How empty the house must be without her. I was so sick, I could not go to Nantes. A short vacation at Couvrelles in the fall, that was all I could afford. Couvrelles deserted now—except for Jaquette Argou, who insisted on staying. Poor girl, alone to receive an invading army."

Bayle let him speak. There was nothing he could say to relieve the deep sadness in his friend's heart.

Théophile looked at his watch. "Time to go to the Salpêtrière and see my 'children,' and the Salpêtrière is not around the corner. It's a good thing I like to walk."

Bayle watched the small silhouette disappear between

the trees. "Thirty-three years old and unhappy," he murmured.

In June 1814, Paris was all aglow with the return of the monarchy and Théophile saluted the accession of Louis XVIII as a token of peace. His patients still scattered in the provinces, his "children" back in their villages, he felt free to take a vacation. In August he went to Quimper.

His feelings were roused as he approached his beloved birthland. Shortly before Vitré he knew he was in Brittany. Differences in the scenery told him: the patchwork look of the fields, a mossy Calvary at a crossroad, a granite church steeple showing the sky through the lacy stonework. Brittany at last, after thirteen years of absence.

He found his father living with Marie-Anne. Papa Laennec had not changed. He still wrote poetry. Recently he had sent a sample of his literary talent to the King, welcoming him to the throne of his forefathers. He still entertained but not as lavishly as before. The would-be debtors were wiser and people snubbed him. He had attempted a reconciliation with his wife but she had ignored his moves.

As of old, he took his "glorious son" around. The Pomperys, still at Quimper, gave Théophile news of Couvrelles. The house and the park had suffered from the occupation. Jaquette, when faced with a horde of Cossacks, had had a heart attack.

"Poor Jaquette," said Théophile, "there is no one to make her laugh now."

After a week's rest he went to Kerlouarnec. He found the place in sad condition. The roof had caved in, the walls around the orchard had crumbled, the pastures needed care, and weeds were growing everywhere; part of the land had been taken by an unscrupulous neighbor.

Immediately he established the exact boundary of his domain and recovered what belonged to him. Then he outlined the necessary repairs. He added a first floor and an attic to the low house. A pointed turret that encased the stairway gave character to the plain building. Next he inquired about trees and grazing land, and, with the thoroughness that was his, he soon could outdo architects and farmers.

A project that was to occupy him for the rest of his life was the draining of the salt marshes at Cosquer, near Pont l'Abbé. In the course of an excursion he had been attracted by an area of desolate land. Twice a year the equinox tides flooded it through a narrow inlet. He thought of rehabilitating it and bought a farm in the vicinity.

He returned to Paris in October after a short visit to Nantes. He was happy. A few more years and he would

lead the life of a gentleman farmer free from financial
worries. Marie-Anne was assured of a life income, his
father's position was secure. The King had ratified the appointment made by the Emperor.

Two months later came a series of catastrophes. Papa
Laennec lost his position. Someone had found a letter addressed to the Convention, congratulating its members for
having voted the King's death. The signature of Théophile
Marie Laennec was in first place. The compromising docu-
ment was forwarded to Louis XVIII with immediate result.

In March 1815 the Emperor debarked from Elba. On
April 11, Papa Laennec was reinstated but not for long.
His poem to the King, in which he called Napoleon the
Usurper, was brought to the Emperor's attention and on
the third of May he was crossed off the list of officials.

Uncle Guillaume, who had first sympathized with the
Revolution and later became an admirer of the Emperor,
had openly expressed his distrust of Louis XVIII. When
Louis reascended his throne after the short-lived imperial
return, he discharged Dr. Guillaume Laennec from his hospital duties and ordered him to be deported.

Théophile acted at once. Through his efforts Uncle Guillaume was spared but Papa Laennec was not restored to his
position. Feeling responsible for his father, Théophile promised him a pension and engineered a reconciliation with his
wife.

Overtaken by the political fever so prevalent in those days, Théophile published a pamphlet entitled: "Is the return to feudalism to be feared most under a king or under a Bonaparte?" Wiser than his father, he did not sign it.

The year 1816 began sadly. In January, Jean Cruvelhier wrote an "Essay on pathological anatomy," dedicated to Dupuytren. It was the forerunner of a treatise on the same subject. This affected Théophile. Hopes of publishing his own *Pathological Anatomy* vanished. As always, bad news undermined his health. Asthma, headaches, digestive troubles reappeared.

On May 11, 1816, Bayle died of pulmonary tuberculosis.

"Disappointments, disillusions, sorrows, loneliness. I have nothing to expect of life any more," grieved Théophile. "Teaching and research are closed to me. Kerlouarnec and Cosquer, that's all that remains to give a meaning to my latter years. Medicine? A disappointment. We are powerless before disease and death. The search for the truth? An illusion. It wanes before we reach it."

CHAPTER 17

S hortly after Bayle's funeral, Théophile was walking along the quays of the Seine. Brooding over the death of his best friend, he paid no attention to the hubbub of the city. He yearned for a respite from responsibility, he longed for the peace of his own Kerlouarnec. Absorbed in his thoughts, he had not noticed a man waving at him from afar. "Eh, Laennec!"

Brought back to reality by the sound of his name, he looked up and apologized for not having recognized Becquey, assistant to the Minister of the Interior.

They exchanged a few words, both deploring the untimely loss of their mutual friend. "This makes four vacancies," Becquey said, counting on his fingers, "Beaujon, Enfant-Jésus, Necker, and now Charité. Since I am general administrator of the Paris hospitals, I'll have to get busy and fill them soon."

Théophile smiled politely and was about to take his leave

when Becquey exclaimed, "By the way, Laennec, would you like to be chief at Necker?"

The words hit Théophile. He repeated as if staggering under a blow, "Chief of service at Necker?"

"Yes. I feel you have been treated unfairly and it is time to correct this injustice. One word and you are named."

Théophile answered in a low voice, "Too late."

"Too late? When you are in your prime? Let's see, you are . . ."

"Thirty-five."

"And you speak like an old man."

"I am an old man," said Théophile gravely. "My health is not good and I'm planning to retire soon while I can still hope for a few years of peace and comfort."

Becquey insisted. "Don't disappoint me. You have the post tomorrow if you say yes today."

"Give me time to think about it."

"Don't think too long. The minister wants to sign the decree of nomination before going on his vacation. Laennec, don't disappoint me."

Becquey gone, Théophile made a few unsteady steps and sat on a low wall. The shock had been too much. He could hardly breathe. In confusion thoughts flashed in his mind: more responsibility when he was trying to lighten his load . . . Necker, what an opportunity for him . . . Kerlouarnec, peace among its trees . . . the briar-covered

moors . . . teaching, research, the goal of his life at hand,
and it had come too late. Five years, even two years earlier
he would have welcomed the offer.

"Too late," he repeated. "Medicine has brought me
many a day of happiness. I must quit before it disappoints
me." Disappoint . . . Becquey's last word. It would not
be fair to disappoint him. A glimpse of Necker surged before his eyes. A beautiful garden, trees, flowers . . . like
a bit of Brittany. . . . His chance to teach. He saw himself surrounded by students. Among them Ambroise and
Mériadec. He would train them and make them heirs to
his knowledge. Medicine was calling once more.

He did not sleep that night. He weighed the pros and
cons and little by little Kerlouarnec's moors faded before
the neatly curtained beds of his service . . . *his service.*

At dawn he wrote his acceptance.

On September 4, 1816, an official letter confirmed his
nomination.

He went to Necker the same day. The mother superior
of the Sisters of Charité who ran the hospital took him
around. "Your service, *Monsieur le docteur,* contains one
hundred beds. One ward for the men, Salle St. Joseph, and
three for the women: St. Louis, Ste. Suzanne, and St.
Vincent."

One hundred beds! Life was good to him. He could have

hugged Becquey, the minister, the mother superior, all the world.

He bowed respectfully and left, hiding his emotion.

It did not take long for Théophile to organize his service. Every morning he appeared at the hospital, invariably dressed in black, knee breeches, a wide-brimmed hat, a white cravat, and a watch chain from which dangled charms and trinkets. He had always liked jewelry.

At nine he made his rounds, lectured in Latin, and visited the autopsy room. He was strict and he was kind. He demanded comprehensive and exact histories but never forgot the patients' side. "Don't torture them with prolonged examinations. Don't tire them." Diseases of the lungs interested him particularly. So little was known of them.

"It is important to make a diagnosis after death," he said one day, "if it teaches us to relate findings on the cadaver with symptoms on the living for future reference. Remember, we must treat, so we must know. A thorough history, a thorough examination, plus the synthesis of our past experiences give us a first lead.

"In the diseases of the lungs some symptoms are obvious: fever, cough, expectoration. These are clues, that is all. It is up to the physician to investigate further. I'll review now the different means of exploration at our disposal.

"First, the succussion that was described by Hippocrates. It will enable you to detect large effusions of liquid in the pleura. You have seen me do it. The technique is simple. You take hold of the patient's shoulders, shake him rapidly, and you may hear the shock of the fluid against the walls of the thorax. This, without forgetting a careful measurement of the two sides of the chest, will tell you you are dealing with a pleurisy.

"Next I'll mention the percussion of Auenbrugger. Its value cannot be denied. It has been described by my master, Dr. Corvisart, to whom goes the honor of reviving it.

"There is another method of exploration which, unfortunately, is forbidden in many circumstances. It consists of listening. All of us have put our ears on a chest to confirm death after the heartbeats could not be felt by the hand any more.

"About 1550, Ambroise Paré, who first ligated arteries, used this method. He noted that 'if there is mud or liquid in a thorax the ear can perceive a noise similar to that of a half-filled bottle when it is shaken.'

"This method was known and used in the Middle Ages. An old Flemish engraving proves it.

"Going back further, Hippocrates, to whom we owe so much, wrote that the sounds of the heart can be heard by contact of the ear to the chest.

"This is objectionable for several reasons. It is uncomfortable for the physician, distasteful sometimes, difficult if the patient is obese, and improper if the patient is a woman.

"I have used it occasionally when it was feasible but I would not advocate its universal practice. The secret of an accurate diagnosis regarding heart and lung ailments is beyond our reach at the present time. Let's hope for a way of perfecting it someday."

A week later, Théophile had seen his last patient. No call to make that afternoon. A short time to himself. He looked at some notes. "This should interest Mériadec," he thought. "He has chosen an interesting subject for his thesis—epidemics. I must help him. He has the makings of a good physician."

Angélique knocked at the door.

"Another patient," sighed Théophile, "and I had hopes of being free for a while. Come in, Angélique."

"I'm sorry to disturb you, monsieur. When you were with your last patient someone came and asked that you go and see his daughter. Here is the address. You've seen her before. She has heart trouble and the poor thing is quite young."

"Thank you," answered Théophile, amused at his servant's interest in his patients. "I'll go. I'll probably be late for supper."

"I'm used to it," grumbled Angélique.

Alone, Théophile looked for the card on which he had recorded his previous findings. "A difficult diagnosis. If I could only listen to her heart, but she is not thin and she is a girl."

He took his hat and cane and went out. The weather was pleasant; he was in no hurry and decided not to call a cab. His walk led him through the gardens of the Louvre. Once there, he strolled leisurely. He liked the stately palace, its trees, its flowers. A wing was under repair and bricks and timber were rotting, unattended, a good spot for the street urchins. A group of young boys surrounded a long beam they had balanced on a stone.

Théophile observed them. "A strange game," he thought. Two boys were posted at each end of the plank. One had put his ear against the wood while the other was scratching at the far end. Bursts of laughter exploded. "Wonderful!"

"My turn!"

"No, mine."

"Hey, I've scratched long enough, let me listen."

Théophile approached. "What are you doing?"

"We are playing at listening, m'sieu."

"May I join in your game?"

"Of course. Hey, you, let the gentleman listen. I'll do the scratching."

Théophile removed his hat and put his ear against the beam. The scratching came to him distinctly. He signaled the boy. "Now tap lightly with your finger, not with your nail."

The light strokes sounded like drumbeats.

"I should have known it!" he exclaimed. "Solids are better conductors than air. Thank you." He grabbed his hat and literally ran away.

The boys looked at each other and one said, pointing at his forehead, "A bat up there."

Théophile could not wait. He signaled a hansom and gave the patient's address.

"But it's around the corner, monsieur," said the driver, "one minute's walk."

"Never mind, rush."

He climbed the stairs in one jump and pulled the velvet cord of the doorbell with such energy that he almost tore it away.

The patient's father greeted him. "Dr. Laennec, we are so thankful you came."

"You seem out of breath, Doctor," said the mother. "Why don't you rest before seeing our daughter?"

Théophile, usually very courteous, asked abruptly, "Can you give me a copybook?"

"You wish to write? A new one of course."

"Unimportant. I want a thick one and a piece of string."

Both his hosts were bewildered. The same thought had come to their minds: "Queer, to say the least."

"Will this do? It is my youngest daughter's class notes."

Théophile rolled the sheets tightly, bound them with the string, and went to the patient's bedroom. Before asking any questions, he put one end of the paper cylinder against the girl's chest and rested his ear on the upper side. He closed his eyes and listened. Like the scratching on the plank, sounds rose through the cylinder with clarity: the soft swish of the lungs' expansion, the drumming of the heart. What a method of exploration! The heart, the lungs were speaking to him.

After a while he raised his head. "Your daughter is not in danger," he said. "Rest and fresh air will cure her. Good-by."

Still holding the rolled sheets, he took his hat and stepped toward the door.

"May I have my daughter's copybook, Doctor? She needs it."

"Of course." Théophile apologized and left.

It was past dinnertime but he did not give a thought to the waiting Angélique; he called a cab and went to Necker. The concierge could not believe his eyes when he saw Dr. Laennec running in at such a late hour. "Must be some emergency," he told his wife.

Théophile entered Salle St. Joseph. Everything was quiet. Sister Ste. Geneviève was distributing pitchers of warm milk from a cart she was pushing along. She opened her eyes wide at the sight of the chief.

"*Bonsoir, ma sœur*. May I have a copybook, please, and a piece of string?"

"I don't think I have a new one," said Sister Ste. Geneviève foraging through drawers, "and will some thread do? Black or white? That's all I can find here."

"Never mind, Sister, an old copybook will do as long as it is thick, and I hope your thread is of good quality."

His face tense with anticipation, Théophile went to the first bed and put the cylinder on the man's chest. A storm of râles * filled his ear. Unmindful of the ironical smiles, he kept going from one patient to another. Here, the heart sounds were soft like the passing of air through a small opening. Fine râles like hair rubbed between fingers, coarse râles like bubbles bursting through a liquid, all the symphony of normal and abnormal sounds came forth through the crude instrument.

Trembling with joy at his discovery, Théophile left the hospital reluctantly.

A renewal of activity seized him and through his painstaking research lung pathology took shape. From the overall label of phthisis emerged distinct entities: cancer of the lungs, pulmonary edema, emphysema, dilatation of the bronchi. And he came to the conclusion that the sixteen

* A râle is an abnormal wheezing sound in the lungs.

or twenty kinds of phthisis were but the different manifesta-
tions of the same disease, pulmonary tuberculosis, in various
stages of evolution.

However he was not satisfied with the paper cylinder
and, to perfect his instrument, he had a lathe installed in
his apartment. He experimented with different woods and
every conceivable length and shape. He finally evolved a
hollow tube of beechwood, twelve inches long, with a flange
or flat projection at each end. A stem or obturator could be
inserted at will to make it solid. Modestly he kept calling it
"the cylinder." Some suggested "pectoriloque" from the
Latin *pectus* (chest) and *loqui* (to speak).

Uncle Guillaume proposed "thoraciscope."

When Théophile presented it to the Academy of Medicine on February 28, 1818, he named it "stethoscope" from
the Greek words *stethos* (the chest) and *skopein* (to examine). His "Memoir on auscultation through acoustic instruments" was received with praise.

Tired, plagued with headaches and his "old asthma," he
kept going. He, who needed long hours of sleep, had to
curtail them to see more patients, write his *Treatise on
Mediate Auscultation,* and make stethoscopes on his lathe.

In July, anxious to devote more time to the completion
of his book, he closed his office for the summer and, the day
after he had written the last word of his treatise, he left
for Brittany, accompanied by Mériadec.

CHAPTER 18

The prospect of going back to Brittany gave Théophile such a new surge of energy that he talked of walking from Paris to Orléans. Mériadec dissuaded him from trying it even from Paris to Versailles, and they took the coach. To have passed through Nantes would have taken too long and they headed for Douarnenez without even a detour to St. Brieuc. Mériadec was anxious to reach their destination. His cousin's health necessitated it.

The trip took the last of Théophile's vanishing strength and when they arrived at Douarnenez he collapsed. His host and Mériadec nursed him for a week. He improved and only then did Mériadec consent to leave for Nantes. Théophile went to Kerlouarnec.

The repairs were far from finished. Still, part of the house was inhabitable and Théophile chose to live there. Immediately he resumed his favorite pastime, walking. As in his younger years he roamed through moors and woods

with his dogs, Kiss and Mustache. How he enjoyed contacts with the peasants. He loved to drop in for a chat, sit
before a bowl of cider, and converse in the rugged tongue
of the Celts. Anything Breton interested him. He collected
old songs, legends, fairy tales of the "little people of the
moors," the *korrigans*. He watched the men of the sea repair their nets and mend their sails. He discussed everything from fishing to the culture of potatoes. His advice
was solicited on many problems. Did not a man ask him if
the burning of the seaweed in a cove would scare the fish
away?

Toward the middle of October the rainy season and the
need for money brought his gentleman farmer's life to an
end. He was dreaming of costly projects for Kerlouarnec
and Cosquer and only his practice could provide for the expense. Furthermore, his book had to be edited and sold.

He returned through Nantes, where his uncle greeted
him with undisguised admiration.

"I have part of the manuscript with me," said Théophile,
"but no sketches. I had to leave some chapters with Dr.
Toulmouche, the illustrator."

"I'll read what you have here," said Uncle Guillaume,
"but first give me a broad outline of the book."

Théophile laughed. "I can see that you want a complete
lecture on my *Treatise on the Mediate Auscultation; or
Treatise on the Diagnoses of the Diseases of the Lungs and*

Heart through This New Method of Exploration. That's the title."

Uncle Guillaume nodded approvingly. "Clear and complete."

"I wrote the preface in Latin and dedicated the work to the Faculty of Medicine. I begin with a review of the methods already known: inspection, palpation, succussion, percussion, and direct auscultation. Then I come to the mediate auscultation."

"Heart and lungs, of course."

"Of course, and I did try to use my cylinder for other things. Fractures, for instance, give a crackling sound when mobilized. I listened to liver abscesses, to stones in the bladder. I even devised a means of educating the deaf and dumb with my good cylinder."

Uncle Guillaume leaned forward, his eyes watching Théophile admiringly.

"Next, a classification of all the diseases of the lungs and pleura through their clinical symptoms, their pathology and causes, without forgetting the treatments.

"I am the first to have identified bronchial asthma as an entity."

A spell of coughing interrupted him.

"You should rest," said Uncle Guillaume. "Talking tires you."

Théophile shook his head. "I'm not tired. Here is the

next chapter. You'll be interested in the report I made on the transmission of both the spoken and the whispered voice as an aid to diagnosis. Now let me add this, which I have not written in these pages: we have no means of treating tuberculosis, call it phthisis or consumption as you wish. This is proved by the countless remedies that have been recommended. I think I'll end this chapter by saying: 'Although the cure of tuberculosis can be effected by nature under certain circumstances still undetermined, it cannot—' "

"It cannot be done by medicine."

Théophile corrected him. "It cannot *yet* be done by medicine but I have hope in the future."

Emotion and pride prevented Uncle Guillaume from making any comment. Théophile continued, swept on by his own enthusiasm: "The second part of the book deals with diseases of the heart and the circulatory system. I have perfected a chapter on cirrhosis of the liver, of which I am justly proud. It is an extensive and comprehensive study of that type of degeneration of the liver. As is my rule, I begin by describing the alterations in the organs involved because they are less variable and more positive than the symptoms. These are not entirely reliable. Some are common to many diseases. That's what makes medicine difficult and fascinating—the art of diagnosis." And Théophile's eyes sparkled with the flame his uncle recognized as the same he had seen one evening in his library when a fourteen-year-old boy said, "I want to be a physician."

During the week he spent at Nantes, Théophile spoke of his approaching retirement, a project that did not meet with Uncle Guillaume's approval. "How can you think of leaving Paris when you are beginning to know fame? Your book might bring you a professorship with a pension later and you could save more if you work another ten or fifteen years."

"I'll never last that long," said Théophile with a bitter smile. "Do you know my schedule? I get up at seven. I see patients before I go out. Then Necker until eleven, and from that time on I make calls in all the sections of Paris."

"When do you eat?"

Théophile shrugged his shoulders. "When and where I can. After dinner, another round of calls. Some afternoons I have consultations at home."

"Less tiring than climbing stairs."

"Yes and no. I like a respite, no matter how short, and a breath of air between patients. Being shut in gives me violent headaches."

"When do you find time to write?"

"In the precious sixty minutes I keep for myself between ten and eleven, my bedtime."

Théophile stretched his legs, looked at the ceiling, and

sighed. "I envy those who practice in small towns or even in villages. They don't need to fulfill social obligations. These boring ordeals steal valuable time that could be employed to better aims." Sitting straight, he looked at his uncle and said in a firm voice, "I give myself one, maybe two years, and my decision is final, I retire. I hope I'll last until then."

Uncle Guillaume could not understand his attitude. He called his nephew a hypochondriac, his ailments imaginary, and his premature retirement an arbitrary decision.

On November 13, 1818, Théophile returned to Paris and the hectic life he despised took him in its claws.

Mériadec visited him daily. One evening in the spring of 1819 he found him at his lathe, ankle-deep in wood shavings and, as usual, greeted him in Latin: "*Quid novi* [What's new]?"

Théophile tossed a stethoscope in the air and caught it adroitly. "Good news," he said. "My treatise is sold. Brosson and Chaudé have accepted it under excellent conditions."

"Then give a contract to a carpenter to turn out your cylinders."

"No," said Théophile, caressing the wood of an unfinished stethoscope with an expert finger. "I enjoy making them and furthermore I can't afford to pay a carpenter."

"What are these excellent conditions, may I ask?"

"You may," replied Théophile, pushing the treadle gently to smooth out a flange. "I sold two editions, which means thirty-five hundred copies. I'm to receive seven thousand francs six months after the publication of each edition. The book will be published in July, in two volumes."

"It's excellent, you are right."

"Especially when Bichat sold the four volumes of his *General Anatomy* for only three thousand francs. So, as soon as I have corrected the proofs, I retire."

Mériadec interrupted him. "Don't speak of retirement. We all need you."

"Kerlouarnec and Cosquer need me and I need them also."

Théophile got up and staggered on his feet. A sudden spell of dizziness had seized him. Mériadec helped him to sit and watched him with anxiety. Théophile's respiration had become labored and rapid. When he breathed more easily he said, "Won't you understand why I want to retire while there is still time to do it?"

℘ CHAPTER 19

When he announced his retirement officially, Théophile had to face Uncle Guillaume's objections once more and his father's ire. "What do I hear? My famous son is deserting his lady fair, Glory, for a few acres of untilled land. Now it will be easier for you to say, 'I can't help you, my dear Papa. I barely manage to subsist on the meager income from my farms.' "

Such a letter was no aid to Théophile, who, brokenhearted, was tearing away from many ties, hospital connections, friendships. Even his guardian angel, Angélique, had to be dismissed. He was afraid that because she was not a Breton she might be ill at ease in a strange place.

Every day brought more distressing experiences in their finality. He sold his library, gave his collections of pathological specimens to the School of Medicine, and sent the furnishings of his apartment to Rouen to be forwarded by boat to Douarnenez. On October 8, 1819, he left Paris.

"I don't want to hear about medicine any more," Théophile declared as he climbed into the carriage. His young companion, Yves de Saint-Alouarn, smiled and so did all the friends to whom he repeated this assertion.

On the eleventh he was at Nantes to hold Christophe's daughter, Louise Théophile Laennec, at the baptismal font.

At the end of October he reached Douarnenez and was at Kerlouarnec the following day.

From then on his letters spoke only of wood paneling, doors, windows, and locks, except that every time he wrote Mériadec he asked him "to please try to collect these long-overdue accounts."

Cosquer was very much on his mind. He planned to close the inlet by means of two dikes with a system of valves to allow a small river to run toward the sea at low tide; at high tide, they would reverse themselves and dam the incoming waters.

He wanted to occupy Kerlouarnec as soon as possible but his household furnishings did not arrive until February, in a pitiful condition.

When spring came everything was settled and he went to Quimper . . . to hold a few consultations.

In July he went on horseback to visit his father, who was still at St. Brieuc. The days of the long walks were gone. He found Papa Laennec as sprightly as ever, his wife very much in love with her poet of a husband, and the house as hospitable as of old.

Papa Laennec spoke casually of the two or three lawsuits he had on his hands and dwelt at length on the poems he addressed regularly to the King.

Reassured as to their lot, Théophile left them and kept going from one place to another. When he returned to Douarnenez after an absence of six weeks he had traveled five hundred miles on horseback.

An imposing number of letters awaited him. Among them were several from Mériadec, and they were discouraging. The cylinder was the target of many jokes. The treatise was highly criticized and not much in demand. Many stethoscopes still lay in the shop. The medical magazines were either cautious in their judgment of the new method or frankly hostile. A rare few dared to praise the treatise.

In spite of all the antagonism, mediate auscultation was fast progressing in the world, in England, Germany, Italy, Spain, Russia, even in the remote Americas.

Slighting fame and critics, Théophile kept roaming the moors, ordered seeds and grains to be planted, and supervised the pruning of his trees. His head covered with a wide-brimmed hat, he manned a hoe or a spade or mixed mortar with the workers. And he who had said, "I don't want to hear of medicine any more," was often asked to see patients and never refused. His fees were scaled from nothing up, nothing being the most frequent.

A letter he wrote to Christophe spoke of a Monsieur d'Argentré, from Douarnenez, who had paid for his consultation with a five-foot-long cod, a twenty-two-square-foot flounder, two lobsters, and a basket of shellfish. "A remarkable fee," was Théophile's appreciative comment.

He sent to Dr. Récamier an article on "The practice of medicine in Brittany" and agreed to give advice to physicians by mail.

Occasionally he went to Quimper, at Dr. Ollivry's request, and one day was asked to see a patient way out in the country.

"Last stage of phthisis," Dr. Ollivry explained as they were driving to the man's house. "Nothing you can do but his family insists that you examine him."

"I came to help you," said Théophile when he entered the sick man's room.

"Ah, *monsieur le docteur,*" sighed the patient, trying to lift his head from the pillow. "If you cure me, the Lord will bless you and your family."

"Tell me, how do you feel?"

"Very bad. An awful pain in my right side, a cough that kills me, and I'm burning all over, especially in the evening."

Théophile helped the man remove his nightshirt and looked carefully at his thorax. He percussed both sides, up and down and again front and back.

"Dullness on the right," said Dr. Ollivry in Latin. "His whole lung is invaded by tubercles."

Théophile had taken a stethoscope from his pocket.

"What's that?" said the patient. "A tool to cure me?"

"Perhaps," answered Théophile with a smile.

He auscultated him for a long time, made him cough, made him count aloud and again in a whispered voice.

"Ollivry," he said, "this man has no tuberculosis but a large quantity of pus in his pleura."

He disregarded the polite doubt in his colleague's eyes and continued, pointing with his finger to illustrate his explanation. "On inspection, enlargement of the right side of the chest. On percussion, dullness as you noticed also, from the base to practically the apex of the lung. I could not hear the respiratory sounds over that area. Egophony is present under the clavicle . . ."

Seeing a bewildered expression on Ollivry's features, he explained, "Egophony, literally the voice of a goat, is the nasal and quivering deformation of the spoken voice through the wall of the chest. It can be heard only at the upper level of the fluid. Below, there is no egophony and the whispered voice is transmitted in the whole area. It is what we call whispering pectoriloquy. The heart is deviated and the liver is pushed down. It's a typical purulent pleurisy."

He had spoken in Latin and, shifting to Breton, Théophile addressed the man. "Would you like to drink a bowl of cider tomorrow?"

A spark of hope shone in the patient's eyes. *"Monsieur le docteur,* I've lost my taste for cider but if you cure me I think I could find it again. I used to outdrink most of my friends."

"Have you a trocar * with you," Théophile asked Ollivry, "and a basin?"

Ollivry handed him a trocar with hesitation. "You do it," he said with a touch of doubt concerning his friend's diagnosis.

"Courage," Théophile said to the patient, "and think of the bowl of cider you'll have tomorrow."

Deftly he plunged the trocar between the ribs near the base of the right lung, withdrew the obturator, and a thick liquid spouted out.

News of the "miraculous" cure spread with the speed of light and the appreciative patient was not the last to praise Dr. Laennec between bowls of cider.

Happy, his health improved, Théophile roamed the

---

* A surgical instrument for puncturing cavities to remove the fluid therein. It consists of a hollow tube with a snugly fitting core whose point protrudes beyond the beveled tube. Once inserted, the core can be withdrawn to allow evacuation of the fluid.

moors with his dogs. He felt so much better that he abandoned riding a horse and resorted to his old mode of transportation, walking. Returning to Paris was far from his
mind but the repairs at Kerlouarnec and the erection of the
dikes at Cosquer were making a serious dent in his savings.
Mériadec had a difficult time collecting long-overdue accounts. The treatise did not sell because of the indifference
of the editors. And another disappointment added itself to
the long list of frustrations that had plagued Théophile.
He had expected to obtain the Experimental Physiology
Prize. It was awarded to someone else. It would have brought
him twelve thousand francs. As a consolation, he was given
a thousand francs. His name had come last on the roll.

The thought of going back to his Parisian practice began to implant itself seriously.

In January 1821, Christophe wrote him that there was
a possibility he would be named professor at the Faculty.
About the same time an editor asked him to reprint his
article on human parasites and inquired what had become
of his *Pathological Anatomy*.

The hospital administration, which had granted him a
leave of absence, began to demand his return and an attack
on his writings by another Breton, Dr. Broussais, strength-
ened his decision.

Afraid of the exhausting days ahead, he wrote to Christophe:

I'll limit my practice to consultations in my office and will try to spend Saturdays and Sundays in the country. I think my health will hold under such an arrangement. As to a professorship, I would not accept it. The task of preparing lectures would be too strenuous for my head and there are days when my asthma won't let me speak for an hour or two. However, I'll return to Paris.

At the news, Mériadec went to Brittany to help him. Of the family, he alone realized his cousin's poor state of health.

⟮ CHAPTER 20

Théophile and Mériadec arrived in Paris on November 15 and took residence at the Hôtel du Bon La Fontaine, 18 Rue de Grenelle. Théophile did not want to lease an apartment. "I must first see if I'll be able to stand the strain."

At Necker he was greeted with affection, and the reopening of his informal lectures during rounds attracted enthusiastic followers. Patients began to fill his waiting room in such numbers that he asked Mériadec to help him carry on his practice.

Steadfastly he had refused to associate medicine and politics; he was averse to intrigues and ambitious scheming. However, when Dr. Hallé offered to have him named physician to the Duchesse de Berry, spouse of the King's nephew, he did not want to offend his friend and accepted. On January 1, 1822, in court costume, he was introduced to his royal patient.

Recognition, honors, a substantial income, his health

holding well—he had everything to be happy, but Théophile was not happy.

Loneliness weighed on him. One by one his friends had departed: the charming Annick de Pompery had died in 1820, Corvisart in 1821, Hallé shortly after presenting him to the duchess, and soon after came the news of Uncle Guillaume's death. While reading Christophe's letter, a profound emotion overwhelmed Théophile. Uncle Guillaume, whose devotion to medicine had oriented his own life. Uncle Guillaume, who had guided and encouraged him. Uncle Guillaume, to whom he owed all he had, all he was.

Deeply affected by the news, Théophile tried to allay his sorrow in a renewal of activities.

Hallé's death had left vacant a chair at the Collège de France, and it was coveted by many for its unusual prestige. The old institution, created by François I in 1530, had kept its independence from the university and, true to its charter, its teaching embraced all branches of human knowledge.

Politics, jealousy, internal strife played against Théophile and he was not elected. Irked by the unfairness of the vote, the Minister of Public Instruction, Monsieur Corbière, appointed him professor and royal lecturer at the Collège de France and signed the decree on July 31, 1822.

Four months later politics again threatened to enter Théophile's life. Trouble had been rampant at the Faculty since the King had named his chaplain, the Abbé de Frayssinous, Grand Master of the university. At the opening of the classes, on November 18, the students rioted, stoned the windows, and the cry: *"A bas Louis XVIII, vive Napoléon,"* burst forth.

The King answered swiftly. On November 21 he dissolved the Faculty. A member of the Royal Council of the Public Instruction, Monsieur Sylvestre de Sacy, resigned.

Corbière called Théophile to the post but he declined. After a conference with the minister, he consented to reorganize the teaching at the Faculty of Medicine, which was more in accordance with his views. The suggestion that he become dean met with his refusal.

A month later Théophile's service was transferred from Necker to the Charité. Now he was in charge of five wards instead of four.

Tired of living at a hotel, in need of larger quarters, he took an apartment with Mériadec at 23 Rue du Cherche-Midi and looked for a housekeeper.

"Why didn't you think of our distant cousin Jaquette Argou?" Mériadec asked him. "She is alone since Monsieur de Pompery's death. You know her, she is pleasant, honest and furthermore," with a teasing gleam in his eyes, "she is fond of you."

Théophile agreed it would be an ideal arrangement and

Jaquette was offered the position. She accepted without delay.

Their meeting was filled with unexpressed emotion which they both tried to restrain. For Théophile, her presence evoked the past and those who were gone. For her, it brought a renewal of the attraction she had felt the day Théophile surprised her sewing in the living room at Couvrelles.

"How he has changed," she thought. "How thin, how pale, how worn out he looks." The trinkets dangling from his watch chain reminded her of his fondness for jewelry. As of old, he was dressed impeccably.

Théophile was observing her. The sad expression that was always hers had carved lines around her mouth, her hair was gray at the temples. She looked older than her age.

They avoided talking of the happy days of the past and Théophile gave her a brief outline of his occupations. "You won't see much of me. Every day, except Thursday and Sunday, I am at the Charité from ten to twelve. Tuesday, Thursday, and Saturday I lecture at the Collège de France at one-thirty. Three times a week I'm examiner at the Faculty. When I'm home I give consultations or I prepare my lectures."

"How can you stand such work?" exclaimed Jacquette.

"I wonder . . ." said Théophile, and then changed the tone of his voice: "Jaquette, I used to make you laugh at Couvrelles. Do you think I could do it now?"

A sketchy smile lifted the corners of her mouth and she said timidly, "I think so, *monsieur le docteur.*"

Théophile looked at her sternly. "No *monsieur le docteur* for me. Call me anything you like from old monkey to Cousin Théophile, but, please, no formality."

For a second Jaquette seemed bewildered by his severe expression, then she laughed frankly. "Thank you for the permission. I'll use Cousin Théophile, if you don't mind, and not—not the other."

Théophile joined in the mirth. "I'm satisfied that I can still make you laugh. Now, Cousin Jaquette, this home is yours."

And Jaquette Argou became Théophile's housekeeper, to the comfort and delight of the two men.

"You can hardly hear her," said Mériadec. "She goes around like a little mouse."

"She never shows any irritation either," said Théophile, remembering Angélique's outbursts and the reputation of watchdog that was hers among his patients.

In the evening she was always invited to sit in the living room and, while sewing, she listened to medical discussions between the two cousins.

"Upon my word," Mériadec said one day to Théophile, "I think Jaquette is in love with you."

"We have passed the age of even dreaming of it. We both are over forty, don't forget it."

When Mériadec was not home, Théophile insisted that she sit with him and he took pleasure in telling her of his activities.

"I have a new idea," he told her one day.

Jaquette lifted her eyes from the cloth she was mending. "I'm interested," they seemed to say.

"If we knew the cause of phthisis we could cope with the situation. We can't cure it and Nature does sometimes. I've tried to find out. Our remedies are useless. I've experimented with whiffs of chlorine, frictions with all sorts of liniments. So far, fresh air seems to give the best results. What do you think, Dr. Jaquette?"

Jaquette blushed and, without interrupting her sewing, said, "It's cheap and easy to obtain."

"Fresh air has always improved my asthma. It's good for everybody."

"At least you follow what you preach. You live with open windows in any kind of weather."

"A fact has impressed me. At Douarnenez there is a remarkably low number of phthisics. Six in four thousand inhabitants. The sea must have something to do with it. This gave me the idea of strewing seaweed around the beds of tubercular patients. I may even try infusion of seaweed."

The seaweed treatment did not prove of any value and Théophile reflected with melancholy, "Another cause for criticism and irony among my detractors." For at that time he was under sharp attacks from Dr. François Broussais, another Breton, born at St. Malo.

They had first met in Corvisart's service. Both Bretons, they should have become friends according to the rules but, from the beginning Broussais had only contempt for *"le petit Laennec."* Jealousy, perhaps, and a hatred of all he labeled Chouans were at the root of his feelings.

His father and mother had been killed by fanatic royalists on Christmas Eve, 1795, and in his eyes Laennec, from Quimper, could not be anything but a reactionary, a Chouan, and all Chouans were responsible for that tragedy.

St. Malo was a corsair haunt. For centuries, out of its port had sailed those dreaded sea rovers who were attacking all ships for booty. During the American War of Independence they preyed on the British and continued to do so during the French Revolution. François Broussais, a most courageous man, had served as a surgeon on a corsair ship.

After saving some money, he went to Paris to complete his medical studies and became a doctor in 1803. Private practice did not interest him and he joined the army. In 1814 he was named professor at the Val-de-Grâce, a military hospital in Paris.

From his years at sea, he had kept the manners of a buccaneer. Mériadec said he was always swinging an ax as if grappling an enemy ship.

Brutality, eloquence, partiality were the characteristics of his personality.

In 1818 he and Théophile met again at a patient's bedside. He looked with scorn at the cylinder Théophile put to use and the fact that *"le petit Laennec"* was right did not enhance their friendship.

Théophile had been inclined to sympathy toward him. He had followed the rule. Broussais was a Breton.

When, in 1821, the ex-corsair published "Considerations on the medical doctrines generally accepted," an article signed by Dr. Laennec gave a detailed and impartial analysis of the work. But when Broussais reduced all pathology to inflammation and gastroenteritis, Théophile refuted his theories, cautiously at first.

". . . Dr. Broussais, a physician whose opinions are well founded except that they tend to be excessive."

Broussais was not going to lose such an occasion to swing his ax. He answered with sharp criticism of the *Treatise on the Mediate Auscultation* and condemned Bayle for not having seen everything.

Théophile replied, "No doubt he has not seen everything. This is beyond any man's range, but what he saw, he saw well. There are few books in which there is less to correct than in his."

In the second edition of his *Considerations on the Med-*

ical Doctrines, Broussais rejected all of Laennec's discoveries. "Tubercles, bronchial dilatation, asthma, pleurisy, they are all due to one thing, irritation." And he called Laennec an explorer of corpses, more interested in performing autopsies than in treating his patients. He even hinted that he let them die for the sake of opening their cadavers.

The *Annals of Physiological Medicine,* edited by Broussais, tore Dr. Laennec to pieces. He was accused of not accepting the new concept that tuberculosis was contagious; his seaweed treatment was laughed at, even his manners and the way he dressed were criticized.

Eusèbe de Salle, in the *Journal universel,* described him thus: "Laennec has the patience of a Chinese. He can take an idea and dig into it, forgetting everything else. He is behind our epoch and his place should have been, not in a nineteenth-century faculty, but in a fourteenth-century university. His so-called discoveries show a retrograde step, not progress."

Broussais, his ax in his hand, continued his assaults. "I feel that I can accuse Dr. Laennec of bad faith. He claims that my opinions are excessive without refuting them. I must attack Dr. Laennec in the interest of France and humanity."

Théophile, without losing his temper, replied, "I have great esteem for Dr. Broussais's talent, in spite of all I am going to tell of his errors and of his manner of attacking those who are not of his opinion. I am asking him to believe in the expression of my true feelings of admiration for his achievements."

The polemic was to continue until Théophile's death.

<◇>CHAPTER 21

In September 1824, Théophile announced he was going to take a vacation. His temporary stay in Paris had lasted two years—two years of constant toil without rest. As soon as he had finished his duty as examiner at the Faculty, he and Jaquette headed for Kerlouarnec. He took great pleasure in showing her his house, the improvements he had made, the dikes at Cosquer, and he enjoyed her admiration for his beloved homestead.

"We are here for two months," he had said.

"May this be true," she had answered.

They had not been there one week when a letter came from Bordeaux. Dr. Laennec was called in consultation by a rich Spaniard and the fee was imposing.

"I'll go," said Théophile. "It's a matter of a few days."

"Unless you get involved in demonstrations of the cylinder."

Jaquette was right. No sooner had Théophile seen his

patient and diagnosed a cavity in his lung than the St. André Hospital organized a series of lectures on the stethoscope by Dr. Laennec. He was asked to follow rounds, he was asked to give consultations. The short absence he had foreseen dragged into a fortnight, then another, and summer was over when he returned to Kerlouarnec.

Jaquette was appalled at his appearance but they had to go. He allowed himself one day's rest, then they left for Nantes.

Together they went to Petit-Port, they walked along the banks of the Erdre. "Here Uncle Guillaume and I collected plants and flowers. Here I fell off our little boat. I was a good swimmer then. In this cove we often admired the sunset."

Lost in memories of the past, Théophile seemed to have forgotten his companion when she put her hand on his arm. "Thank you," she said in a low voice, "for telling me of your young days. It brings me closer to you."

"We'll come again another year, won't we, Jaquette?"

Her heart filled with apprehension for Théophile's health, she answered, "Of course we will."

The morning they were leaving, Christophe took Théophile aside. With visible embarrassment, he asked his cousin if he had not heard anything about Jaquette. Seeing Théophile's surprise, he tried to dismiss the subject.

Théophile insisted. "What about Jaquette?"

"I don't want to hurt your feelings but I'd better speak frankly. People are beginning to wonder about your friendship."

"Jaquette is above any reproach."

"I don't doubt it and be assured that I'm not of those who wonder."

"You mean that some evil tongue is misjudging our association?"

"I'm afraid so, and I would make evil tongue plural and I would include Brest, Quimper, and Kerlouarnec."

Théophile was shocked. He could scarcely believe that he had been the target of wild gossip and was completely unaware that calumny was rampant. In thinking back, details that he had not associated with malevolence surged in his memory: hidden smiles at their approach, a finger pointed at them from behind quickly drawn curtains, a word here and there. And he felt keenly responsible for the fact that Jaquette's name had been defamed.

He spoke little during the trip to Paris and the afternoon they arrived home he pretended he had a headache, an excuse for retiring early. After a light supper he apologized and got up.

"Your room is ready," said Jaquette.

"How did you do it?" Mériadec exclaimed. "You have been here a couple of hours, you have fed us—and very

well, I must say—and the apartment looks as if you had
not been away."

Théophile said nothing. He smiled at Jaquette with appreciation as her eyes followed him with affectionate anxiety,
then he went to his room.

A quick glance showed everything in order. There was
a bunch of violets, his favorite flowers, on the table, the
inkstand of heavy Quimper crockery had been filled, the
windows were open as he always requested, and flames
leaped gaily in the fireplace.

He sat at his desk, rested his forehead between his hands,
and closed his eyes. "This must stop," he thought. "I've
exposed Jaquette to slander. It would be wise to separate."

He let his hands fall on the table and opened his eyes.
The comfort of the room surrounded him with Jaquette's
untold devotion. The fragrance of the violets was like a
caress.

Separate from Jaquette . . . How he would miss the
silent expression of her feelings. Life without Jaquette . . .
At once the apartment seemed empty. He revolted against
the idea. "I could not let her go." He tried to motivate his
reasons. "She has no family, no money, and a separation
would not stop people from talking. It might even encourage them. Her few friends could snub her. She must
stay here always."

Always . . . and the real cause for wanting her near

him always glowed in his heart. He refused to accept it. "I'm deeply attached to her." Then the truth imposed itself. "I'm in love with Jaquette."

He repeated, "In love and forty-four years old. It will be amusing to watch my friends' reactions . . . and my enemies'. They'll be the first to call me an old fool." This made him laugh and a sober thought crossed his mind. "How will she receive my proposal? She may call me an old fool too." A twinge of anxiety made him stop laughing.

The thought of having to propose to Jaquette kept him awake all night, and when morning came he really had a headache. He refused to see any patients and entrusted Mériadec with the task.

In the afternoon he called Jaquette to his office.

"Could this wait?" she said. "I have so much to do."

"That can wait. What I wish to tell you can't."

"May I bring my sewing?"

Théophile hesitated for a second. "No," he said. He did not want Jaquette's eyes diverted by a menial task. He wanted to read the expression in them.

She sat where patients sat and said laughingly, "Don't forget to bill me, Doctor."

The serious look on Théophile's face made her stop short. Mingled with the serious look, she could detect an unusual touch of concern and affection.

"Jaquette," said Théophile slowly, "did you ever think of getting married again?"

"Cousin Théophile, at my age?"

"Age means nothing. I've found that the heart does not feel the passing of the years."

With the intuition of a woman in love, Jaquette sensed the hidden meaning of the words.

"If you had a proposal, Jaquette, what would you say?"

She understood. Théophile's eyes were pressing for an answer. She hesitated and the wait seemed endless to Théophile. Then she turned her head away and spoke in a lighter tone. "I would say no. I have nothing to offer. I'm not young, I'm not elegant, and I know I've never been pretty."

"You said yes once."

Jaquette blushed. "My marriage had been arranged between our parents."

"Couldn't you arrange a second marriage yourself?"

Jaquette looked straight at Théophile. Her lips moved and, out of timidity or pride, she stiffened.

Théophile felt it. He rushed his question. "Jaquette, would you marry me?"

Her face glowed, then she closed her eyes as if afraid they would belie her answer and shook her head negatively. Emotion prevented her from speaking.

Théophile repeated his question.

"No," she said dryly. She got up to hide her tears and ran away.

Again Théophile felt the same strange twinge in his heart.

The following day life continued as if nothing had happened. Jaquette was her usual prompt, efficient self, possibly more distant. Her eyes avoided Théophile's.

He was out all morning and came home in the early afternoon. As he entered, he saw a trunk near the door and he met Jaquette carrying a heavy load of clothing.

He acted as if he had not noticed anything, greeted her cheerfully, and went to the living room. He opened the window, took a book, and pretended to read.

A discreet knock at the door, and at his "Come in," Jaquette was before him.

Théophile dropped his book and looked at her. Her eyes were red and she seemed embarrassed. "Would you . . . like . . . a cup of tea?" she asked, the words coming out with difficulty.

"Not now. Sit down. I've things to tell you."

"So do I," she murmured so low that it was easy for Théophile to pretend he had not heard.

"I saw an editor today and I'm going to revise my *Treatise on Auscultation*. He's ready to publish it."

Disconcerted and interested by the turn of the conversa
tion, Jaquette listened silently.

". . . and I'm preparing an answer to Broussais's latest
attack. That is not all. I'm going to publish a case of oblitera-
tion by a blood clot of the vena cava, iliac, and saphenous
veins on the same side. Would you care to hear my answer
to Broussais? I have a first draft here."

As he reached for the paper Jaquette got up and, with
the boldness of a timid person, almost screamed, "I'm going
away." Then she burst into tears.

Théophile went to her and gently pushed her hands from
her face. "Where are you going, Jaquette?"

"I don't know. To Brittany—somewhere."

"Very well. When you come back we'll set the date of
our wedding."

"But . . ."

"You want to do it now? It will make me very happy."

"Cousin Théophile, I ought to go. I can't stay after . . .
after . . ."

Théophile took her in his arms. ". . . after you refused
yesterday, but what about today? I need you, Jaquette, I
need the warmth of your affection, I need your care, your
understanding. Why did you say no?"

"Who am I to be chosen? You are a celebrity, a man
whose name is worshiped, whose advice is sought after."

"Shhh," said Théophile. "And you are the woman I love. Jaquette, I repeat my question: will you marry me?"

Barely audible, a faint yes died on her lips.

Mériadec was the first to hear the news. He embraced Jaquette and made her dance around. "Hurrah for my new cousin!"

"She's already our cousin to the three hundred and fifty-ninth degree," interrupted Théophile.

"Those degrees mean nothing. She'll be my first cousin now."

After dinner Théophile wrote his father, somewhat fearful of his reactions. They were excellent.

The next one to be notified was Christophe. Théophile, a respectful son, had waited for his father's answer before announcing his forthcoming marriage to others. He concluded his letter to his cousin by saying: "And dear Papa thinks it is exciting, wonderful, marvelous. This leads me to believe that my decision is not entirely reasonable."

They were married in Paris, on the sixteenth of December 1824, first at the city hall of the 6th arrondissement, according to the French law, and the religious ceremony was held at St. Sulpice on the same day.

It was followed by a simple luncheon. Around the couple gathered the four witnesses, all prominent names in medicine. The only member of the family present was Mériadec.

The newlyweds were toasted with champagne and the best man, Baron Charlet, read letters of congratulation. Among them was one from the Duchesse de Berry.

Théophile did not mention the overwhelming piece of poetry his father had sent to the "loving couple," in which he compared them to all the illustrious lovers of history.

❧ CHAPTER 22

The following months were happy ones. Théophile had changed for the better. His health had improved, he was exuberant, he looked younger. Planning to stay another ten years in Paris, he moved to 17 Rue St. Maur.

Good news from Kerlouarnec made him feel optimistic. The house was entirely finished. The works at Cosquer were going well. The revision of the *Treatise* was approaching completion. If it had not been for the ever present bickering with Broussais, life would have been peaceful.

Happiness did not last. In the spring after their marriage Jaquette became gravely ill and for a time Théophile despaired of her life. Slowly she regained her health but her illness had brought an end to the early hopes of maternity that had given them such joy.

About the same time distressing news came from Cosquer. A landowner in the vicinity had obtained a temporary injunction to stop the erection of the dikes. He had complained to the Administration that they would interfere with the tides and hinder fishing.

The trial ended in Dr. Laennec's favor, but the irate landowner did not accept the judgment and twice more tried to interfere with the construction.

Théophile, indignant at his neighbor's ill will and anxious to see the completion of the dikes, became restless. Insomnia, headaches, digestive troubles beset him. His "old asthma" returned.

The editor pressed him. He wanted to publish the revised *Treatise* by April 1826. Facing a deadline, Théophile forsook his practice and worked feverishly at his manuscript between lectures and rounds. When the book went to the printer he took to his bed. His temperature rose, violent pains in his chest made breathing difficult and coughing painful. A sore throat aggravated his condition.

Jaquette and Mériadec called Dr. Récamier. He ordered bloodletting, which relieved Théophile temporarily.

One morning he appeared depressed, and to Mériadec, who was trying to comfort him, he said, "Phthisis."

"No. Bronchitis, sore throat, but no phthisis."

Théophile shook his head. "Do you remember a paragraph in my book where I describe how, in certain grave illnesses, the heart sounds are perceptible at a distance?"

Mériadec nodded.

"Last night I observed the fact on myself."

"You felt the beating of your arteries in your ears."

Théophile smiled with irony. "You can't fool me. My ears are well trained." He stopped Mériadec's protests and said, "Give me my manuscript."

"You don't need to show me that paragraph. I remember."

"No. I want to record my own observation."

At the end of April he felt well enough to consider going to Kerlouarnec, but another disappointment set him back. On Cuvier's advice, he had applied for the Montyon Prize in physiology, to be awarded by the Academy of Sciences. His application was late and the Academy rejected his candidacy.

Immediately nervous symptoms reappeared. He could not eat, he could not sleep, and fever did not leave him.

He asked Mériadec and Dr. Récamier to auscultate him and to describe what they heard. They did not dare tell him the tragic truth. His own diagnosis had been correct. He was in an advanced stage of pulmonary tuberculosis.

The last of May was taken up with final arrangements. He asked for a leave of absence from the Faculty and from the Collège de France. He called on the Duchesse de Berry, who gave him the Cross of the Order of St. Michel, the oldest decoration in France. He bid *au revoir* to his friends, left his patients to Mériadec's care, and on May 30 headed for Brittany with Jaquette and a servant.

The trip began under pleasant skies but two days later the weather became rainy and cold. Théophile, a prey to high fever, had to rest. After forty-eight hours he insisted he could resume his journey and they went on.

At Rennes he suffered from an abscessed tooth. His fever abated after it was extracted. Jaquette tried to get him to stay for a while longer but he refused.

Shortly before they reached Vannes they met with an accident. The horses fell into a ditch and their carriage turned over. Nobody was hurt but this delayed them once more. Théophile wanted to avoid punishment for the driver. This obliged them to remain three days at Vannes. Arriving at Quimperlé on the seventh of June, he fainted. One of his former students, established in the town, ordered him to bed for at least a week. Théophile did not obey. They kept going. On the ninth they were at Kerlouarnec.

It was midafternoon. A sky of delicate blue set off the white walls of the house. Its turret pointed boldly upward. Roses were blooming along the fence. In the distance, cows and sheep were grazing.

Neighbors had gathered to greet the famous doctor and his wife. They were shocked at his appearance. With difficulty he alighted from the carriage and, leaning heavily on Jaquette's arm, walked through the garden. While she and the servant were getting the house ready he sat outside. At last he was home. He tried to fill his lungs with the life-

giving breeze of his beloved Brittany and a shattering
cough stopped him. He put his handkerchief to his lips. A
red spot tinted it.

The following evening he asked Jaquette to write at his
dictation and inform Mériadec of his condition. "My
strength is half of what it was when I left Paris. I have lost
considerable weight. High fever at the end of the day. Less
perspiration at night. Cough and expectoration about the
same. Appetite not improved. . . ."

Courageously, Jaquette wrote the pitiful words, control-
ling her tears.

"Now I want to write to my father. It is no secret from
you that my financial situation is not brilliant. I must ask
him to consent to a reduction in the allowance I give him.
Will he understand? My poor father . . . he has as
much sense of responsibility as a ten-year-old."

Remissions alternated with relapses. He yearned for the
outdoors and, to keep him from fatigue, Jaquette had an
armchair built on wheels. Every day, thanks to her in-
genuity, he was able to look at those cherished landscapes,
filling his heart with the beauty of the sea, the wonders of
the sunset, the peace of the woods.

At the end of June, Christophe and Ambroise came for
a short stay. Their arrival lifted Théophile's spirit so much
that his appetite returned. He even took several walks with
them.

Ambroise wrote Mériadec that his condition was desperate. "Terminal stage of pulmonary tuberculosis."

After they left, Marie-Anne arrived from Quimper and Papa Laennec announced his forthcoming visit to discuss an increase in his allowance. This upset the whole household. At eighty, the old gentleman had not lost his talent for sowing seeds of trouble wherever he went. It was pointed out to him that a trip at his age would be too tiring and, to everybody's relief, he agreed to stay where he was and wait for better news before coming. His incurable optimism refused to see his son as he was.

And Théophile was growing weaker and knew it. He asked for and obtained a cancellation of his lease in Paris to reduce his expenses. The draining of the Cosquer marshes was costing more than anticipated. He tried to sell some bonds. They were valueless. To relieve his worries, Mériadec bought them at a high price without his knowledge.

One day when Théophile was discussing money matters with Jaquette and urging her to buy more land at Cosquer, she made him understand that this was beyond their means and, unintentionally, through an awkward answer, disclosed the fictitious sale.

That same evening fever mounted to a new high and Théophile became delirious. Jaquette, in tears, blamed herself for having brought about the relapse and refused to leave his bedside day or night.

For four days he lay semiconscious, confused and irrational at night.

On the thirteenth of August, in the middle of the afternoon, he woke up from his torpor. Jaquette leaned over and put her hand on his burning forehead. He recognized her. The shadow of a smile lighted his face, then, slowly, he removed his rings from his fingers and made a feeble effort to put them on the table.

"Théophile, what are you doing?"

"Another would soon have to do it," he whispered. "I want to avoid giving him this sad duty."

These were his last words.

He was buried at Ploaré three days later.

Behind the hearse walked his family and those he had loved, the Bretons.

Under the granite cross that extends its protective arms over the little cemetery, a simple tomb reminds those who pass by that:

Ici repose
René Théophile Hyacinthe Laennec
Médecin de S.A.R. Madame la Duchesse de Berry
Lecteur et Professeur en Médecine au Collège de France
Professeur de Clinique à la Faculté de Paris
Membre de l'Académie Royale de Médecine
Chevalier de la Légion d'Honneur
Né à Quimper en 1781
Mort à Kerlouarnec le 13 Août 1826